Science and Technology Concepts for Middle Schools™

Energy, Machines, and Motion

**Student
Guide
and
Source
Book**

D1312321

NATIONAL SCIENCE RESOURCES CENTER

The National Science Resources Center (NSRC) is operated by the Smithsonian Institution and the National Academies to improve the teaching of science in the nation's schools. The NSRC disseminates information about exemplary teaching resources, develops curriculum materials, and conducts outreach programs of leadership development and technical assistance to help school districts implement inquiry-centered science programs.

SMITHSONIAN INSTITUTION

The Smithsonian Institution was created by act of Congress in 1846 "for the increase and diffusion of knowledge...." This independent federal establishment is the world's largest museum complex and is responsible for public and scholarly activities, exhibitions, and research projects nationwide and overseas. Among the objectives of the Smithsonian is the application of its unique resources to enhance elementary and secondary education.

THE NATIONAL ACADEMIES

The National Academies are nonprofit organizations that provide independent advice to the nation on matters of science, technology, and medicine. The National Academies consist of four organizations: the National Academy of Sciences, the National Academy of Engineering, the Institute of Medicine, and the National Research Council. The National Academy of Sciences was created in 1863 by a congressional charter. Under this charter, the National Research Council was established in 1916, the National Academy of Engineering in 1964, and the Institute of Medicine in 1970.

STC/MS PROJECT SPONSORS

National Science Foundation
Bristol-Myers Squibb Foundation
Dow Chemical Company
DuPont Company
Hewlett-Packard Company
The Robert Wood Johnson Foundation
Carolina Biological Supply Company

Science and Technology Concepts for Middle Schools™

Energy, Machines, and Motion

**Student
Guide
and
Source
Book**

National Science Resources Center

THE NATIONAL ACADEMIES • Smithsonian
Institution

Published by Carolina Biological Supply Company
Burlington, North Carolina

NOTICE This material is based upon work supported by the National Science Foundation under Grant No. ESI-9618091. Any opinions, findings, and conclusions or recommendations expressed in this material are those of the authors and do not necessarily reflect views of the National Science Foundation, the Smithsonian Institution, or the National Academies.

This project was supported, in part,
by the
National Science Foundation
Opinions expressed are those of the authors
and not necessarily those of the Foundation

ISBN 978-0-89278-546-9

Published by Carolina Biological Supply Company, 2700 York Road, Burlington, NC 27215.
Call toll free 1-800-334-5551.

Cover design and illustration by Max-Karl Winkler; cover photo, Gemini double-racing roller coaster at Cedar Point Amusement Park, by Dan Feicht/Cedar Point Amusement Park/Resort, Sandusky, Ohio. Printed in the United States of America

CB787821206

Energy, Machines, and Motion

MODULE DEVELOPMENT STAFF

Developer/Writer
Dane J. Toler

Science Advisor
John Layman
Professor Emeritus of Physics
University of Maryland

Editor
Linda A. Long

Contributing Writers
Carolyn Hanson
Linda Harteker
David Marsland
Carol O'Donnell
Kitty Lou Smith
David Wetzel

Illustrators
Dan Sherbo
Max-Karl Winkler

Photographic Research
Carolyn Hanson
PhotoAssist, Inc.

Design Consultation
Isely &/or Clark Design

STC/MS Project Staff

Principal Investigators
Douglas Lapp, Executive Director, NSRC
Sally Goetz Shuler, Deputy Director, NSRC

Project Director
Kitty Lou Smith

Curriculum Developers
David Marsland
Henry Milne
Carol O'Donnell
Dane J. Toler

Publications Director
Heather Dittbrenner

Managing Editor
Dorothy Sawicki

Senior Editor
Linda Harteker

Illustration Coordinator
Max-Karl Winkler

Photo Editor
Janice Campion

Graphic Designer
Heidi M. Kupke

Administrative Officer
Gail Thomas

Program Assistants
Matthew Bailey
Carolyn Hanson

Publications Assistant
Famin Ahmed

STC/MS Project Advisors

Judy Barille, Chemistry Teacher, Fairfax County Public Schools, Virginia

Steve Christiansen, Science Instructional Specialist, Montgomery County Public Schools, Maryland

John Collette, Director of Scientific Affairs (retired), DuPont Company

Cristine Creange, Biology Teacher, Fairfax County Public Schools, Virginia

Robert DeHaan, Professor of Physiology, Emory University Medical School

Stan Doore, Meteorologist (retired), National Weather Service, National Oceanic and Atmospheric Administration

Ann Dorr, Earth Science Teacher (retired), Fairfax County Public Schools, Virginia; Board Member, Minerals Information Institute

Yvonne Forsberg, Physiologist, Howard Hughes Medical Center

John Gastineau, Physics Consultant, Vernier Corporation

Patricia A. Hagan, Science Project Specialist, Montgomery County Public Schools, Maryland

Alfred Hall, Staff Associate, Eisenhower Regional Consortium at Appalachian Educational Laboratory

Connie Hames, Geology Teacher, Stafford County Public Schools, Virginia

Jayne Hart, Professor of Biology, George Mason University

Michelle Kipke, Director, Forum on Adolescence, Institute of Medicine

John Layman, Professor Emeritus of Physics, University of Maryland

Thomas Liao, Professor and Chair, Department of Technology and Society, State University of New York at Stony Brook

Ian MacGregor, Director, Division of Earth Sciences, National Science Foundation

Ed Mathews, Physical Science Teacher, Fairfax County Public Schools, Virginia

Ted Maxwell, Geomorphologist, National Air and Space Museum, Smithsonian Institution

Tom O'Haver, Professor of Chemistry/Science Education, University of Maryland

Robert Ridky, Professor of Geology, University of Maryland

Mary Alice Robinson, Science Teacher, Stafford County Public Schools, Virginia

Bob Ryan, Chief Meteorologist, WRC Channel 4, Washington, D.C.

Michael John Tinnesand, Head, K–12 Science, American Chemical Society

Grant Woodwell, Professor of Geology, Mary Washington College

Thomas Wright, Geologist, National Museum of Natural History, Smithsonian Institution; U.S. Geological Survey (emeritus)

Foreword

Community leaders and state and local school officials across the country are recognizing the need to implement science education programs consistent with the National Science Education Standards to attain the important national goal of scientific literacy for all students in the 21st century. The Standards present a bold vision of science education. They identify what students at various levels should know and be able to do. They also emphasize the importance of transforming the science curriculum to enable students to engage actively in scientific inquiry as a way to develop conceptual understanding as well as problem-solving skills.

The development of effective standards-based, inquiry-centered curriculum materials is a key step in achieving scientific literacy. The National Science Resources Center (NSRC) has responded to this challenge through the Science and Technology Concepts for Middle Schools (STC/MS) program. Prior to the development of these materials, there were very few science curriculum resources for middle school students that embody scientific inquiry and hands-on learning. With the publication of the STC/MS modules, schools will have a rich set of curriculum resources to fill this need.

Since its founding in 1985, the NSRC has made many significant contributions to the goal of achieving scientific literacy for all students. In addition to developing the Science and Technology for Children (STC) program—an inquiry-centered science curriculum for grades K through 6—the NSRC has been active in disseminating information on science teaching resources, in preparing school district leaders to spearhead science education reform, and in providing technical assistance to school districts. These programs have had a significant impact on science education throughout the country.

The transformation of science education is a challenging task that will continue to require the kind of strategic thinking and insistence on excellence that the NSRC has demonstrated in all of its curriculum development and outreach programs. Its sponsoring organizations, the Smithsonian Institution and the National Academies, take great pride in the publication of this exciting new science program for middle schools.

J. DENNIS O'CONNOR   BRUCE M. ALBERTS
Under Secretary for Science   President
Smithsonian Institution   National Academy of Sciences

Preface

The National Science Resources Center's (NSRC) mission is to improve the learning and teaching of science for K-12 students. As an organization of two prestigious scientific institutions—the National Academies and the Smithsonian Institution—the NSRC is dedicated to the establishment of effective science programs for all students. To contribute to that goal, the NSRC has developed and published two comprehensive, research-based science curriculum programs: the Science and Technology for Children® (STC®) program for students in grades K-6, and the Science and Technology Concepts for Middle Schools™ (STC/MS™) program for students in grades 6-8.

The STC/MS curriculum project was launched in 1997. The overall design of the instructional materials and the process by which they were developed are based on a foundation of research. The STC/MS courses were informed by research on cognitive development, teaching, learning, assessment, and the culture of schools.

The STC/MS curriculum materials consist of eight courses. Through these courses, students build an understanding of important concepts in life, earth, and physical sciences and in technology; learn critical-thinking skills; and develop positive attitudes toward science and technology. The STC/MS program materials are designed to meet the challenge of the National Science Education Standards to place scientific inquiry at the core of science education programs. Specifically, the National Science Education Standards state that "...students in grades 5–8 should be provided opportunities to engage in full and partial inquiries.... With an appropriate curriculum and adequate instruction, middle school students can develop the skills of investigation and the understanding that scientific inquiry is guided by knowledge, observations, ideas, and questions." STC/MS also addresses the national technology standards published by the International Technology Education Association.

Informed by research and guided by standards, the design of the STC/MS courses addresses four critical goals:

- Use of effective student and teacher assessment strategies to improve learning and teaching.
- Integration of literacy into the learning of science by giving students the lens of language to focus and clarify their thinking and activities.
- Enhanced learning using new technologies to help students visualize processes and relationships that are normally invisible or difficult to understand.
- Incorporation of strategies to actively engage parents to support the learning process.

The research and development process has included trial teaching and field-testing nationwide with geographically and ethnically diverse student populations, as well as the active involvement of the scientific and engineering communities. This process has ensured that the learning experiences contained in each module reflect current scientific thinking, and are pedagogically sound and developmentally appropriate for students.

The NSRC is grateful to the Smithsonian Institution and the National Academies for their overall project support and for sharing their scientific expertise—critical for the development of world-class products. Support for project staff and the associated work to produce and publish these materials has been made possible by the National Science Foundation, our publisher Carolina Biological Supply Company, and numerous private foundations and corporations, including Bristol-Myers Squibb Foundation, The Dow Chemical Company Foundation, DuPont, the Hewlett-Packard Company, and The Robert Wood Johnson Foundation.

The NSRC would like to acknowledge Douglas M. Lapp, former NSRC Executive Director, for his vision and leadership on the STC/MS project. The STC/MS development staff, under the direction of Kitty Lou Smith, and the publications staff, under the direction of Heather Dittbrenner, working in cooperation with Dorothy Sawicki, Managing Editor for the first four modules, and Linda Griffin Kean, Managing Editor for the second four modules, are to be commended for their creativity, dedication, and commitment to develop these excellent curriculum materials that will be used to improve the learning and teaching of middle school science in the nation's schools.

We welcome comments from students and teachers about their experiences with the STC/MS program materials and recommendations for ways the STC/MS courses can be improved.*

Sally Goetz Shuler
Executive Director
National Science Resources Center

---

*Please forward your feedback and suggestions to STC/MS Program, National Science Resources Center, Smithsonian Institution, Washington, DC 20560-0403.

Acknowledgments

The National Science Resources Center gratefully acknowledges the following individuals and school systems for their assistance with the national field-testing of *Energy Machines, and Motion:*

Atlanta Public School District, Georgia
Site Coordinator: Lela Blackburn, Science Coordinator

Lorrie D. Green, Teacher, J. C. Young Middle School

Stephanie Greene, Teacher, W. L. Parks Middle School

Melanie Robinson, Teacher, West Fulton Middle School

Hands-on Activity Science Program, Huntsville, Alabama
Site Coordinator: Sandra Enger, University of Alabama in Huntsville

Huntsville Area Public Schools
Nana Garner, Teacher, Athens Middle School

Jerry Lindsey, Teacher, Brookhaven Middle School

Sandra Patrick, Teacher, Scottsboro Junior High School

Judy Smith, Teacher, Brookhaven Middle School

Mason-Lake Oceana Mathematics and Science Center, Scottville, Michigan
Site Coordinator: Marsha Barter, Director

Mason-Lake Intermediate School District
Melissa Bansch, Teacher, O. J. DeJonge Junior High School

James R. Beckstrom, Teacher, O. J. DeJonge Junior High School

Mason County Central School District
Jean M. Nicholson, Teacher, Mason County Central Middle School

Montgomery County Public Schools, Montgomery County, Maryland
Site Coordinator: Patricia A. Hagan, Science Project Specialist

Tim O'Keefe, Teacher, Martin Luther King Middle School

Schenectady City Schools, Schenectady, New York
Site Coordinators: Paul Scampini, Coordinator of Science; Ann Crotty, Professional Development Specialist

Beverly Elander, Teacher, Oneida Middle School

Colette McCarthy, Teacher, Central Park Middle School

Fitz Glenn Miller, Mount Pleasant Middle School

Fort Bend Independent School District, Sugar Land, Texas
Site Coordinator: Mary Ingle, Secondary Science Coordinator

Doug Fletcher, Teacher, Hodges Bend Middle School

Ruth McMahan, Teacher, Hodges Bend Middle School

Carl Peters, Teacher, Hodges Bend Middle School

The NSRC also thanks the following individuals from Carolina Biological Supply Company for their contribution to the development of this module:

Helen Kreuzer, Director of Product
    Development
Bobby Mize, Instructional Materials Manager
Evelyn Cummo, Product Developer
Jennifer Manske, Publications Manager
Jonathan Shectman, Editor
Anita Wilson, Designer

Finally, the NSRC appreciates the contribution of
    its STC/MS project evaluation consultants—

Program Evaluation Research Group (PERG),
    Lesley College

Sabra Lee, Researcher, PERG
George Hein, Director (retired), PERG

Center for the Study of Testing, Evaluation, and
    Education Policy (CSTEEP), Boston College

Joseph Pedulla, Director, CSTEEP
Maryellen Harmon, Director (retired),
CSTEEP

Contents

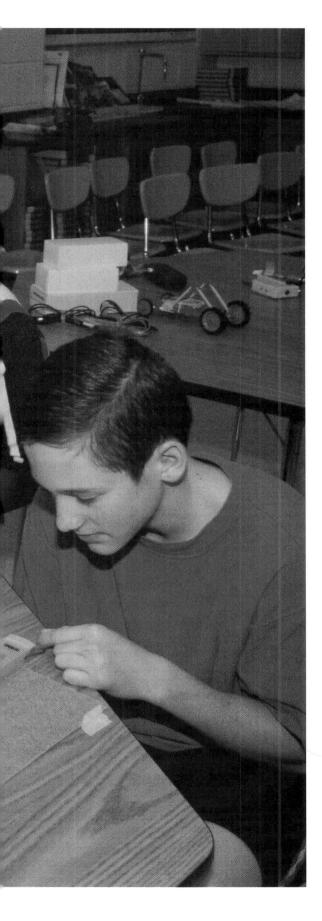

PART 1 Energy

Circuit of Inquiries— A Preassessment

Can you see a machine in this photo? Can you see motion? Can you see evidence of energy? You will explore these topics in this module.

INTRODUCTION

What do you know about energy, machines, and motion? In this lesson, you will complete eight short inquiries about the topics in this module. The inquiries are designed to get you thinking about physical forces, energy transformations, machines, and motion. The observations you make and the ideas you discuss in this lesson will prepare you for the inquiries ahead in *Energy, Machines, and Motion.*

OBJECTIVES FOR THIS LESSON

Perform a series of activities to investigate forces, energy transformations, and machines.

Observe, describe, and hypothesize about the physical phenomena you experiment with in the activities.

Relate your observations to personal experiences.

Getting Started

1. Your teacher will divide the class into pairs of students. You and your lab partner will work together on the eight short inquiries in this lesson.

2. Listen as your teacher reviews the directions for carrying out the inquiries. At your teacher's direction, go with your partner to your first inquiry station.

PROCEDURE

1. At each station, complete the activity described in the directions on the Inquiry Card. The directions are also included on pages 4–8 in your Student Guide. You may want to refer to them later.

2. For each activity, record your observations on your student sheet. Answer the questions in complete sentences.

3. When you finish each inquiry, put everything back the way you found it for the next pair of students.

4. When time is called, move quickly and quietly to the next station.

5. Repeat Steps 1, 2, and 3 for the other seven inquiries.

MATERIALS FOR LESSON 1

For you

1 copy of Student Sheet 1: What We Observe About Energy, Machines, and Motion

Inquiry 1.1
The Single Pulley

PROCEDURE

1. Pull on the string and observe what happens.

2. Describe what you observe. Write your description on Student Sheet 1.

3. On Student Sheet 1, describe a situation where you have seen a pulley or pulleys being used.

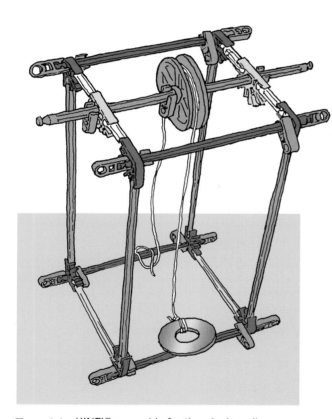

Figure 1.1 *K'NEX® assembly for the single pulley*

Inquiry 1.2
The Pegboard Lever

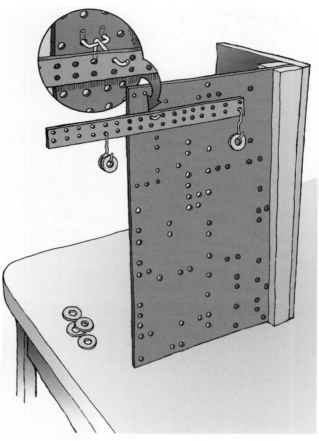

Figure 1.2 *The pegboard lever attached to the pegboard assembly*

PROCEDURE

1. Examine the lever. It should have one washer on the right arm and two on the left, and it should be balanced (see Figure 1.2). On your student sheet, draw a diagram showing the washers and the balanced lever.

2. Leave the washer on the right arm, but remove the paper clip and washers from the left arm. Use the paper clip to attach a different number of washers to the left arm, and try to balance the lever (or nearly balance it). Draw a diagram of your new arrangement.

3. In addition to the number of washers, what did you change to balance the lever?

4. On Student Sheet 1, describe something else you can balance.

Inquiry 1.3
The Hand Warmer

PROCEDURE

1. Put the digital thermometer's shaft between the palms of your hands for 1 minute. Observe the thermometer and record the temperature.

SAFETY TIP
When using a digital thermometer, be careful with the pointed end.

2. Leaving the thermometer between your hands, rub your hands together for a short time. Observe the thermometer as you do this. Stop rubbing your hands and describe what happens to the temperature.

3. Write down another example of how you can produce heat.

4. Each student should perform Steps 1 and 2 if there is time.

Inquiry 1.4
Constructing a Graph

PROCEDURE

1. A bowling ball was released, and the distance it rolled was measured at the end of 5, 10, and 15 seconds.

2. Draw a graph on your student sheet using the measurements recorded in Table 1.

Table 1 Distance the Bowling Ball Traveled Over Time

Time (seconds)	Distance (meters)
5	15
10	25
15	30

3. What does the graph show about the bowling ball's motion?

Inquiry 1.5
Transforming Energy

PROCEDURE

1. Rapidly move the shaft of the generator (motor) back and forth over the stretched rubber band on the books (see Figure 1.3). Watch the lightbulb and describe what you observe.

2. Describe the energy transformations that are taking place.

3. Give an example of another way to generate electricity.

Figure 1.3 *The setup for Inquiry 1.5*

Inquiry 1.6
The Puck Launcher

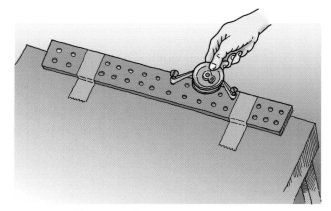

Figure 1.4 *The setup for the puck launcher*

PROCEDURE

1. Put the wheel against the rubber band (see Figure 1.4). Pull the band and puck back about 2 centimeters (cm) and release the puck. Describe the puck's motion.

2. Put the puck against the rubber band. Pull the band and puck back about 4 cm and release the puck. Describe the puck's motion.

3. What force acted on the puck each time it was released?

4. Describe how the puck's motion is different and how it is the same in the two trials.

5. Give an example of a force that acts on an object. What is the force's effect?

Inquiry 1.7
Up the Incline

PROCEDURE

1. Lift the 1.0-kilogram (kg) mass directly to the top of the ramp at the ramp's high end (see Figure 1.5). Describe the size of the force (for example, small, medium, or large) when you lift the mass directly onto the high end of the ramp.

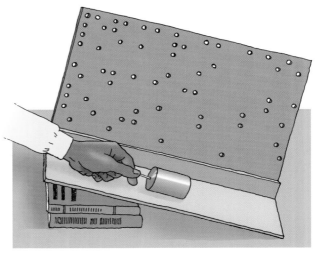

Figure 1.6 *Pulling a mass up the inclined plane*

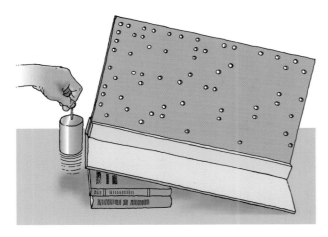

Figure 1.5 *Lifting a mass onto the inclined plane*

2. Put the same 1.0-kg mass on its side at the bottom of the inclined plane, and pull it with a steady force up the incline to the top (see Figure 1.6). Describe the size of the force you exerted or applied when you pulled the mass up the incline.

3. How do the forces—lifting the mass and pulling the mass—compare?

4. Describe another situation in which people use inclined planes.

Inquiry 1.8
Down the Ramp

PROCEDURE

1. Put the car on the ramp's high end (Position 1) and let it go.

2. Describe the car's motion.

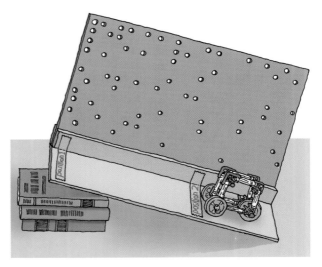

Figure 1.7 *The car and ramp*

3. Put the car farther down the ramp (Position 2) and let it go (see Figure 1.7).

4. Describe the motion you observe.

5. Compare the motions of the two cars and explain why they are different.

REFLECTING ON WHAT YOU'VE DONE

1. Discuss with your partner and then with the class what you have observed and your ideas about your observations.

2. In class, summarize your observations and give examples of similar forces, energy transformations, and machines you have seen outside the classroom. Your teacher will record the ideas on a class list.

Galileo and Experimental Science

In Lesson 1, you made observations, took measurements, recorded and analyzed data, and discussed your findings with your classmates. This probably seems like the logical way to do science—but it hasn't always been the case.

In ancient times, scientists were curious about the world around them. These early scientists often relied too much on general observations and on what previous scientists had done. They were often reluctant to question authority.

About 400 years ago in Western Europe, things changed. A number of scientists began to explore the world around them with a fresh eye. Everything interested them. They looked at things in a new way. They did not just observe things and record information; they experimented to see if their ideas were correct. One of the most famous of these scientists was an Italian named Galileo Galilei.

Galileo was born in Pisa, Italy, in 1564. At the age of 17, he entered the University of Pisa. He planned to become a doctor, but he soon became sidetracked. Galileo began to observe things that were happening around him, and he found them much more interesting than what he heard in the lecture hall.

Galileo Galilei

COURTESY OF THE LIBRARY OF CONGRESS

Even the simplest things could be fascinating. For example, Galileo sat in church and watched a lamp swing from the ceiling. He soon realized that its movements were regular. He could time them with his pulse beat. When Galileo watched different lamps, he discovered that there was a relationship between the time it took for a lamp to swing back and forth and the length of the chain from which it was suspended. He also discovered that a lamp swung back and forth in the same amount of time, regardless of how broad or narrow the swing.

Galileo did not find any immediate application for his observations of the swinging lamp. (That would come later, with the invention of a pendulum clock). But it didn't matter. The experience was important because he had identified and documented a mathematical relationship in a universal event—the swinging of a lamp.

As Galileo became more involved in science, he began to record his observations in notebooks. This was another important distinction between him and earlier scientists. These notebooks, in which he frequently made sketches, enabled Galileo to share his ideas with other

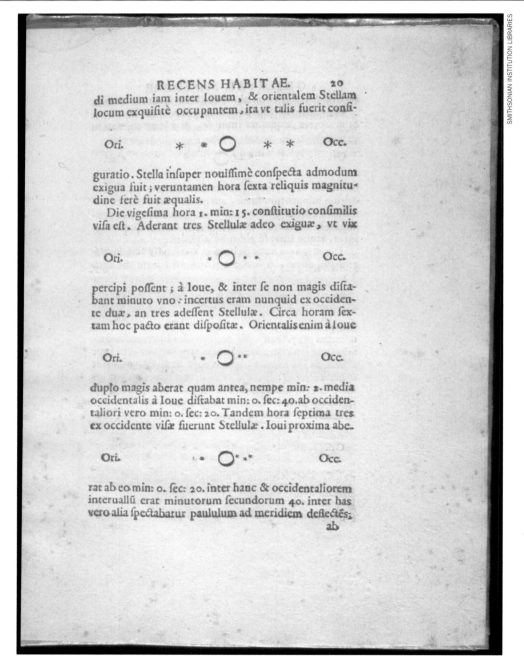

With his telescope, Galileo saw four moons orbiting Jupiter. He studied their motions from night to night and recorded the positions of the moons in his notebook.

people of his time. The notebooks, which still exist today, give us insight into his imaginative and creative mind.

Galileo was a famous inventor. One of his most astounding devices was a military compass that could aim cannonballs at the enemy.

He achieved his greatest fame as an astronomer, however. He built his own telescope. With it, he made observations that revolutionized our understanding of the universe. He saw craters on the moon and thousands of stars in the Milky Way galaxy.

He looked at the planet Jupiter and saw four small points of light circling it. At first, he thought they were distant stars. As he continued to observe and record what he saw, he finally concluded that those points of light were actually moons in orbit around the planet. Today, these moons are called the Galilean moons.

Galileo's ideas sometimes got him into trouble. For example, his observations convinced him that the planet Earth revolves around the sun. (For centuries, people had thought that Earth was the center of the solar system.) This idea was very controversial, especially to leaders of the Church, who put Galileo on trial for heresy and threatened him with torture. To keep Galileo quiet, the Church leaders put him under house arrest for the rest of his life. Galileo could no longer speak out in public, but he remained convinced that his beliefs about the solar system were correct (and, of course, they were).

The Galileo space probe, launched by the National Aeronautics and Space Administration (NASA) in 1989, honored this famous Italian scientist. Its mission is to observe Jupiter and send information back to Earth. The space probe also sends information about the four moons that Galileo first saw in 1609.

To Galileo, these moons were four tiny points of light. Take a look at the pictures from the space probe, below. Do you think Galileo would be pleased to see his moons in such detail? ☐

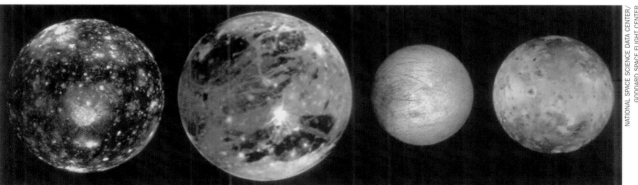

NATIONAL SPACE SCIENCE DATA CENTER/ GODDARD SPACE FLIGHT CENTER

Close-up photos of Jupiter's moons, taken by the Galileo space probe.

Making a Battery

How many different ways do you see batteries used here?

INTRODUCTION

Batteries are used for all kinds of devices today, and they come in all shapes and sizes. Some batteries are so small they could fit on a penny. Others are too big to pick up. What is a battery? What do you need to build one? In this lesson, you will build and test your own battery.

OBJECTIVES FOR THIS LESSON

Build a battery.

Observe what happens when a battery operates.

Describe what makes up a battery.

Getting Started

1. Discuss with your partner what you know about batteries. On Student Sheet 2.1: What Do We Know About Batteries? fill in the first column, "What I Know."

2. With your partner, create a list of things you would like to know about batteries. Write your list on Student Sheet 2.1 in the second column, "What I Want To Learn." Keep this sheet until the end of Lesson 4, when you will fill out the last column.

3. During the class discussion, share your ideas about batteries.

4. Before you start to build the battery, listen as your teacher reviews the Safety Tips for handling materials.

5. Keeping a record of what you do and observe is an important part of the scientific process. Have your science notebook ready to record your predictions and observations.

SAFETY TIPS

Wear safety goggles at all times when working with a battery.

Be careful not to spill any solution from the plastic container. If some does spill, immediately wipe it up with a wet paper towel.

Wash your hands at the end of class.

MATERIALS FOR LESSON 2

For you
- 1 copy of Student Sheet 2.1: What Do We Know About Batteries?
- 1 pair of safety goggles

For you and your lab partner
- 1 blotter paper strip
- 1 zinc strip
- 1 copper strip
- 1 rubber band
- 1 clear plastic container
- 1 grain-of-wheat lightbulb with wire leads
  Copper sulfate solution
  Paper towels
  Pieces of masking tape

Inquiry 2.1
Building a Battery

PROCEDURE

1. To make sure you have all the materials you need to build your battery, compare the materials at your lab station with the items in the materials list.

2. Building your battery requires teamwork. To build the battery, follow the directions in the captions of Figures 2.1, 2.2, and 2.3. Then complete Steps 3 through 9.

Figure 2.1 *Lay the copper strip on the blotter paper as shown.*

Copper strip
Blotter paper

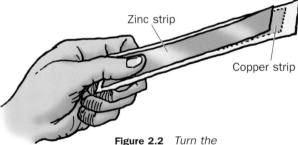

Zinc strip
Copper strip

Figure 2.2 *Turn the assembly so that the blotter paper is on top and place the zinc strip on the blotter paper. Make sure the copper strip is beneath the blotter paper and does not touch the zinc strip.*

Figure 2.3 *Wrap a rubber band around the zinc–copper assembly so that it will stay together. Stand the assembly on end and bend the top of each strip as shown.*

3. Now you are ready to do some tests. Examine the zinc and copper strips and note what they look like. Draw a picture of what your assembly looks like.

4. Is what you have made a battery? How can you use a lightbulb to test whether it is a battery? Describe what you would do in your science notebook.

5. Use your lightbulb and perform your test. Figure 2.4 shows one way to do this. Record your observations.

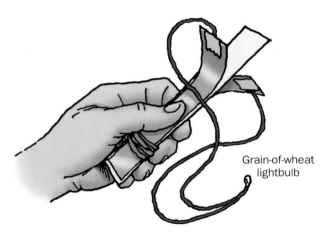

Grain-of-wheat lightbulb

Figure 2.4 *You can attach the lightbulb to the zinc and copper strips with masking tape.*

6. Now fill your plastic container half full with copper sulfate solution.

7. Place the zinc–copper assembly in the solution and wet the blotter paper (see Figure 2.5). Use the grain-of-wheat lightbulb to test whether this setup is a battery. Record your observations.

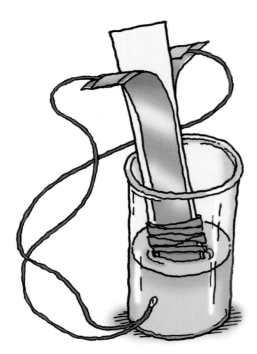

Figure 2.5 *Place the zinc–copper assembly in the copper sulfate solution.*

8. Lift the zinc–copper assembly from the solution, but keep the lightbulb attached. Look at the copper and zinc strips and record your observations of the strips.

9. Lay the assembly on a paper towel, as shown in Figure 2.6, and observe the bulb for a few minutes. Record your observations.

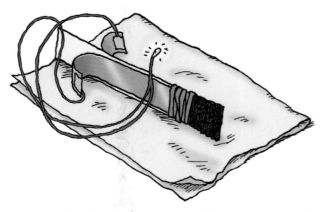

Figure 2.6 *Lay the zinc–copper assembly on a paper towel.*

10. Follow your teacher's directions for cleaning up. Be sure to wash your hands.

REFLECTING ON WHAT YOU'VE DONE

In your science notebook, answer the following questions using the observations you recorded. Then discuss your answers with the class.

A. The goal of this lesson was to build a battery. Did you succeed? Support your answer with evidence.

B. Describe what makes up a battery.

C. What do you conclude from your observations of the zinc–copper strips you placed in the copper sulfate solution?

D. What happened to your lightbulb after you removed the assembly from the solution? How would you explain to someone what happened?

E. In these activities, you probably noticed that the bulb was not very bright. What could you do to make the bulb glow more brightly?

BATTERIES—ELECTRICITY TO GO

© VAN BUCHER/PHOTO RESEARCHERS, INC.

An artist's depiction of Alessandro Volta demonstrating his battery to friends

Take a look at the battery in a flashlight or under the hood of a car. You'll probably see the words "1.5 Volts" or, in the case of the car, "12 Volts." These terms refer to the voltage of the battery, which determines the kinds of devices that can use the battery. For example, when you connect a 1.5-volt battery to a flashlight bulb, an electric current flows through the bulb and provides the energy needed to light it.

"Volts" and "voltage" are named for Alessandro Volta, the Italian scientist who built the first electric battery 200 years ago. Volta's battery was made of strips of zinc and copper, separated by pads that were soaked in saltwater. This crude mechanism, now called a "voltaic pile," produced an electric current.

Shortly after Volta had built the first battery, a British chemist, Sir Humphry Davy, built a much more powerful battery by connecting three voltaic piles. He used this large battery to isolate two elements, sodium and potassium, from compounds.

Encouraged by his success, Davy built an even bigger battery. This one measured approximately 10 meters by 10 meters—probably about the length of your classroom! Eventually he was able to use his "megabattery" to isolate seven elements. Davy's work was an important contribution to the field of chemistry.

Sir Humphry Davy built his giant battery in the basement of Britain's Royal Society. Although no one knew it at the time, Davy's work was dangerous. Potassium and sodium, the elements he was trying to isolate, can explode when exposed to water.

Davy used the results of his experiments to create a new branch of science, called electro-chemistry, which is the study of the relationship between electricity and chemical changes in matter.

Although Davy's battery worked, it wasn't practical for everyday use. Scientists continued to experiment. By the 1880s, they had designed batteries that were portable and inexpensive. Until the invention of the electric generator, batteries were the main source of electrical power. ☐

Sir Humphry Davy

QUESTIONS

1. Compare the battery you made with Volta's battery. How are they similar? How are they different?

2. Davy's batteries were not practical for everyday use. Why? What did Davy do with the batteries he built?

3. Why do some scientists and archaeologists think that Volta was not the first person to build a battery?

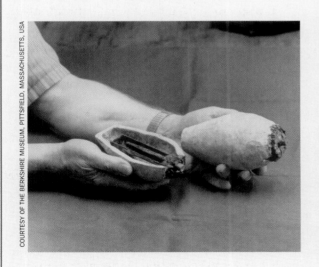

Batteries of Clay

Some archaeologists and chemists think that the first electric batteries may have been clay pots. The metal rods inside the pots were surrounded by a copper cylinder. When a solution was poured into the pot, it became a working battery that could generate up to 2 volts of electricity. Jewelers may have used the current to coat ordinary metals with gold and silver. The clay pots pictured here are models of those found in Baghdad. The real clay pots found in Baghdad are more than 3000 years old.

Wet-Cell and Dry-Cell Batteries

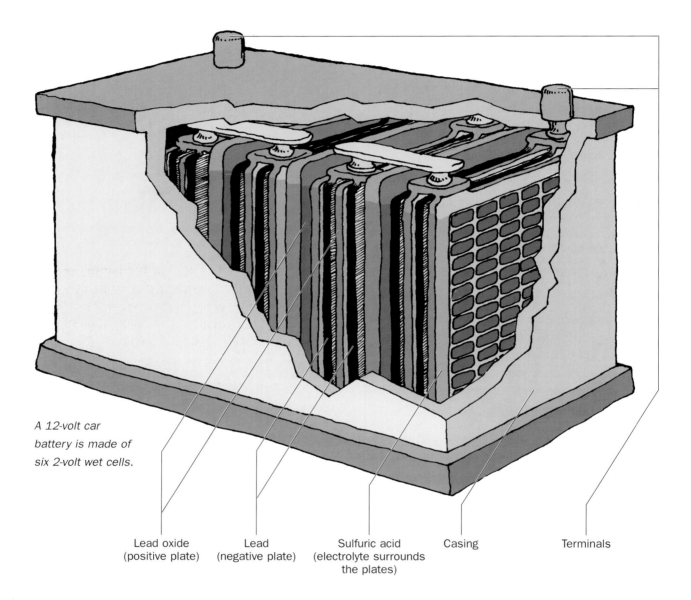

A 12-volt car battery is made of six 2-volt wet cells.

Lead oxide (positive plate) Lead (negative plate) Sulfuric acid (electrolyte surrounds the plates) Casing Terminals

In Lesson 2, you made a battery using two metal strips, called electrodes, and a liquid, called an electrolyte. The assembly of zinc and copper strips placed in a copper sulfate solution is an example of a "wet-cell" battery. It is called "wet" because the electrodes are placed in a liquid. The copper sulfate solution was the electrolyte for your battery. The battery you made is called a cell because it is the basic building block of larger batteries. Connecting cells can make batteries that supply more voltage than a single cell. Many batteries are made by connecting cells. That's what Sir Humphry Davy did when he made his big battery.

A car battery is made of wet cells. It is made of six cells (pairs of metal electrodes with a liquid electrolyte made with sulfuric acid) arranged in a row. The terminals of the battery are connected to the first and last metal electrodes in the row of cells. Connected this way, the six cells provide enough electrical energy to start a car and to supply energy to its lights, radio, and other electrical devices.

But wet cells are not always practical. What kinds of problems would you have if you tried to use the wet cell you made in a flashlight?

The batteries built by Volta, Davy, and other scientists in the 19th century were wet cells. In the late 19th century, a new kind of battery was invented. It is called a dry-cell battery. A dry-cell battery is not really dry, but it has an electrolyte in it that is a paste instead of a liquid. The electrodes and the electrolyte paste are put in a sealed container with terminals connected to the ends of the electrodes. The paste does not spill out if the dry cell is moved around or turned upside down.

The invention of dry cell batteries made batteries portable. It made it possible to use batteries in many devices that were not suited to wet

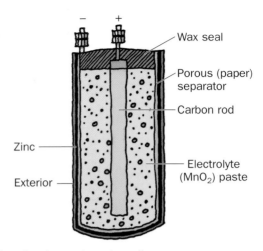

Interior of a zinc–carbon dry cell

cells. Today, dry cells are used in battery-powered toys, flashlights, smoke detectors, radios, CD players, and many other devices. The diagram illustrates what makes up one kind of dry cell. Later in this module you will use dry-cell batteries to run electric motors. □

Rechargeable Batteries

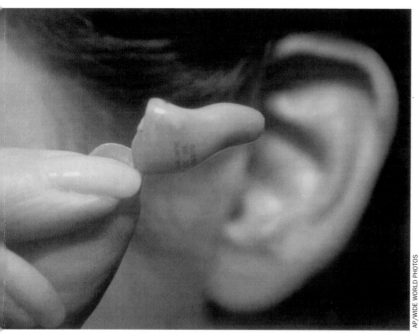

Batteries come in a variety of sizes and shapes. This "in the canal" hearing aid uses very small batteries.

INTRODUCTION

Has someone you know ever parked a car and left the headlights on for a long time? What happened the next time he or she tried to go somewhere? Did the car start? If not, what did your friend do to start it? In Lesson 2, you built a battery. What do you think would happen to that battery if you left the light connected to it turned on for a long time? In this lesson, you will explore answers to these questions.

OBJECTIVES FOR THIS LESSON

Test a battery.

Store energy in a battery.

Identify the energy changes that take place when a battery is connected to different devices.

Getting Started

1. With the class, review how you built your battery in Lesson 2 and what happened when you connected it to the lightbulb.

2. Think about your answers to the questions in the Introduction. Discuss your answers with the class.

Inquiry 3.1
Charging a Battery

PROCEDURE

1. Examine the dry-cell battery at your lab station. Will it light a bulb? Test it and see if it will (see Figure 3.1). Describe your test in your science notebook. What do you conclude about the energy in your battery?

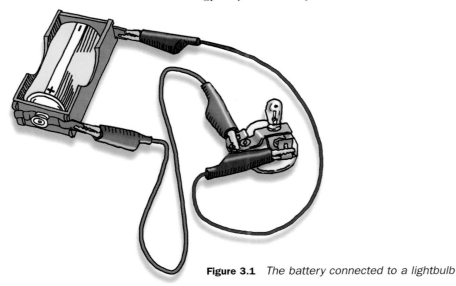

Figure 3.1 *The battery connected to a lightbulb*

MATERIALS FOR LESSON 3

For your group
1 battery charger

For you and your lab partner
1 D-cell battery
1 D-cell battery holder
1 miniature lightbulb
1 miniature lightbulb holder
1 student timer (or clock with a second hand)
1 electric motor with wire leads and alligator clips
1 black insulated connector wire with alligator clips
1 red insulated connector wire with alligator clips

2. You will use a battery charger for the rest of this inquiry. It is important to connect your battery correctly to the charger. Watch as your teacher demonstrates how to connect your battery to the charger safely.

3. Before you begin to work, review the Safety Tips with your class.

SAFETY TIPS

Be careful to avoid electrical shocks when you are connecting your battery to the charger. To avoid shocks, follow these procedures:

• Make sure the battery charger is unplugged when you insert and remove your battery.

• Make sure the batteries are placed correctly in the charger. The positive end of the battery should be at the positive end of the charging bay.

4. Put your battery in the battery charger, as shown in Figure 3.2, and plug in the charger for 3.0 minutes.

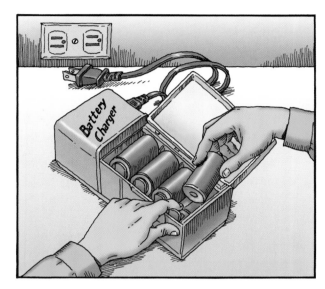

Figure 3.2 *Unplug the battery charger before adding or removing batteries. Make sure the batteries are placed correctly in the charger.*

5. After 3.0 minutes, unplug the charger, remove the battery from the charger, and test the battery with your lightbulb. Record your observations in your science notebook.

6. Leave the lightbulb connected to the battery for at least 10 minutes and record what happens during this time.

7. Now repeat Steps 4 through 6, using the small electric motor in place of the lightbulb (see Figure 3.3). Record your observations.

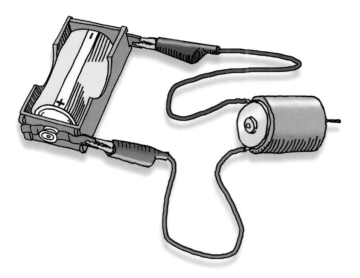

Figure 3.3 *What happens when you connect the motor to the battery?*

REFLECTING ON WHAT YOU'VE DONE

Discuss the following questions with your partner. Record your answers in your science notebook. Be prepared to share your answers with the class.

A. How was your battery different after you attached it to the charging apparatus for 3.0 minutes? Support your answer with evidence.

B. How can you explain your observation?

C. What happened when you left the bulb connected to the battery? Why did this happen?

D. What happened to the battery's energy when you connected it to the lightbulb?

E. What happened when you repeated your experiment with the electric motor?

F. From your observations, do you think the motor or the light needs more energy to operate? Give reasons for your answer.

G. On the basis of your experiences in Lessons 2 and 3, write a description of a battery in your science notebook.

Different Batteries for Different Needs

Batteries come in many sizes and shapes. Some of them are strong enough to supply the electrical energy needed to power a truck; others keep your wristwatch going. Some batteries run constantly, as in the wristwatch. Others, like the ones you put in a photo flash, just have to be ready when needed.

Regardless of these differences in size, shape, and capacity to store energy, all batteries have one thing in common. Each is a container of stored chemical energy that is available and ready to be turned into electrical energy.

It Can't Last Forever. Or Can It?

Batteries are an important part of our lives, and it would be great if they lasted forever. Unfortunately, they don't. When the chemical energy inside a battery is used up, the clock stops, the music dies, or the flashlight goes dark.

At that point, you have two choices. If the battery is disposable, you throw it away and put in a new one. Many batteries today, however, are like the battery you used in this lesson—rechargeable. You connect the battery to an electrically powered battery charger. Electric

The interior of a dry cell

current flows through the battery. Electric energy changes to chemical energy. Within a short time, the battery is ready for action.

Battery Capacity

Why can some batteries store more energy than others can? The capacity of a battery (that is, how much energy the battery will store and generate) depends on what the electrodes and electrolytes are made of, and how much there is of these materials. The power needed to run a device determines how long the battery will operate before it needs to be recharged.

For example, a lithium-ion battery can store more energy than a nickel–cadmium or a zinc–manganese battery of the same size. Laptop computers, which need a steady supply of energy for a long time, operate on lithium-ion batteries. Flashlights, which are turned on for short periods, need less energy than computers do. For them, zinc–manganese dioxide batteries work fine.

Batteries have come a long way since Alessandro Volta assembled his voltaic pile in 1800. The invention of rechargeable batteries was an especially important advance. ☐

The interior of a mercury battery

Stacking cells in series makes a battery with a higher voltage. This 6-volt battery, made of sandwiched layers of nickel and cadmium, is rechargeable.

QUESTIONS

1. What other improvements would you like to see in batteries?
2. How could these design improvements be made?

Storing and Using Energy in a Battery

A young woman recharges the batteries in her 1912 electric car.
In the early years of automobiles, electric cars were popular.

CORBIS/SCHENECTADY MUSEUM: HALL OF ELECTRICAL HISTORY FOUNDATION

INTRODUCTION

In Lesson 3, you charged your battery and tested it with a lightbulb. Everyone in the class used the same charging time. But suppose you and your classmates charged your batteries for different lengths of time. How might the amount of time you spent charging the batteries affect how long they last when you use them to light a flashlight? Lesson 4 will help you answer this question.

OBJECTIVES FOR THIS LESSON

Investigate how the energy stored in batteries depends on the time the battery is charged.

Apply experimental design techniques in conducting an investigation.

Construct a graph of data.

Use a graph to make and test a prediction.

Draw conclusions based on evidence in your data.

Getting Started

1. On the basis of what you did in Lessons 2 and 3, review your definition of a battery.

2. Listen as your teacher reviews how to hook your battery to the battery charger and how to tell whether your battery is charging properly.

3. Suppose you connected the battery to the charger for different amounts of time. In your science notebook, write a hypothesis about how you think the charging time would affect the operation of the lightbulb.

4. Discuss with the class how you can test your hypothesis using appropriate experimental design. Be sure to identify the independent variable and the dependent variable.

MATERIALS FOR LESSON 4

For you
   Your partly completed copy of Student Sheet 2.1: What Do We Know About Batteries? (from Lesson 2)
1 copy of Student Sheet 4.1: Measuring the Energy Stored in a Battery

For your group
1 battery charger

For you and your lab partner
2 D-cell batteries
1 flashlight
1 student timer (or clock with a second hand)

Inquiry 4.1
Charging Batteries for Different Lengths of Time

PROCEDURE

1. Go to your assigned battery charger. Two pairs of students will work at the same charger.

2. Place your batteries in the charger. Follow the safety guidelines and instructions. After charging your batteries for 30 seconds (0.5 minutes), unplug the charger and remove the batteries.

3. Switch the flashlight to the "Off" position. Put the two batteries in the flashlight (see Figure 4.1) so that they line up positive end to negative end. Turn on the switch and start the student timer. Stop the timer when the bulb is no longer lit.

Figure 4.1 *Make sure the flashlight is turned off before you remove the batteries from the charger and place them in the flashlight.*

4. Record the time in Table 1 on Student Sheet 4.1. Later, your data will become part of the data used to calculate class averages.

5. Repeat Steps 2 through 4, charging your batteries for 60, 120, and 240 seconds and discharging them through the light-bulb after each charging. Record the data in your table after each trial.

6. Share your data with the rest of the class. Compute the class average for each trial. Record the class averages in the data table.

7. Construct a graph of class data on Student Sheet 4.1. Follow these guidelines:

A. Decide which variable you controlled—the charging time or the time the bulb stayed lit—when you did the experiment. This is the independent variable; it goes on the *x* axis.

B. Determine the dependent variable from your observations. This variable goes on the *y* axis.

C. Label each axis with the name of its variable and its unit of measure (minutes or seconds). For example, "Battery-charging time (seconds)" and "Time bulb stays lit (seconds)."

D. For each axis, choose a scale that includes all your data points. Make sure to divide the scale on each axis into equal units.

8. Use your graph to predict how long the bulb will stay lit if you charge the battery for 180 seconds. Record the prediction in your notebook.

9. Test your prediction and record the results.

10. With your lab partner, discuss your results and how you can use graphs to make predictions. Be prepared to discuss your results with the class.

REFLECTING ON WHAT YOU'VE DONE

1. Discuss the following questions with your lab partner and write the answers in your science notebook.

A. Discuss with your lab partner any patterns you observe in data that come from class averages. For each trial, why is it better to use the class average instead of results from only one pair of students?

B. Describe the shape of the graph that comes from the class averages. What does it tell you about the length of time the battery was charged and how long the bulb stayed lit?

C. How did you use the graph to make your prediction about how long the flashlight would stay on if you charge the batteries for 180 seconds?

D. How did the length of time the bulb stayed lit compare with the length of time you predicted?

E. Why was it helpful to use a graph to make your prediction? Could you have made your prediction another way?

F. Do your data support your hypothesis? Give evidence from your data.

2. Go back to the chart on Student Sheet 2.1: What Do We Know About Batteries? On the basis of what you have observed and measured in this lesson, fill in the last column "What I Learned." Be ready to share your answers with the class.

Electric Cars: Back to the Future?

Before cars were invented, horses were a common means of transportation. They are still a useful form of transportation today. In some cities, police officers use horses to get through congested car traffic.

engines by hand. This was a big disadvantage. With the starter, gasoline soon became the fuel of choice. There was plenty of it, and it was cheap. More and more people wanted cars. The auto industry grew at an incredible rate. By 1924, electric cars had nearly disappeared from the road.

In 1900, automobiles were not yet a part of American life. A total of 4200 cars were sold in the entire United States in that year. Cars were pleasure vehicles that could be afforded only by the very rich.

That's probably no surprise. But how about this: Of those 4200 cars, only 12 percent were powered by gasoline. The rest were powered by steam or electricity. Electric cars were very popular a century ago. Many used the Edison Cell, a nickel–iron battery. These cars could travel 50 miles on each charge. They reached a speed of 40 miles an hour—not fast by today's standards, but a big improvement over a horse and carriage!

What changed things? The invention of the starter motor. Before the starter was invented, owners of cars that ran on gasoline had to crank up their

Above: *Thomas Edison stands next to his Baker electric car.*

Left: *1928 Ford Model A. Electric cars had to take a back seat to these popular gasoline-powered cars.*

Pollution from gasoline-powered vehicles is a major problem in many cities of the world.

For 50 years or so, things went fine. By the 1970s, however, Americans became worried about gasoline shortages. Environmental groups expressed concern about the effects of fuel emissions on air quality. The U.S. Congress passed "clean air" legislation that imposed new regulations on the auto industry.

One result was a search for alternative fuels. Electricity, used in the first cars, was a natural choice. Manufacturers began to design battery-powered vehicles to replace gasoline-powered cars.

Instead of using chemical energy that has been stored in the form of gasoline, electric cars (sometimes called "EVs," which stands for "electrical vehicles") use chemical energy that has been stored in a large rechargeable battery. When a driver steps on the pedal, a vehicle system controller sends power to an electric drive motor.

AP/WIDE WORLD PHOTOS

A modern electric car

When it's time to recharge an electric car, the owner hooks a charge plug into a 240- or 120-volt charge device. Recharging at 120 volts takes up to 24 hours; at 240 volts, it takes about 6 hours. Some EVs have special brakes that generate electricity instead of heat friction. The brakes stop the car and recharge the battery at the same time!

EVs have three big advantages over gasoline-powered vehicles:

1. They're clean: EVs have no tailpipe emissions. Their engines don't generate fumes or waste fuel while idling.
2. They're quiet: EVs, unlike combustion engines, make almost no sound.
3. They're smooth: Most EVs don't have gears—no jerky acceleration!

Despite these advantages, people are still not willing to switch to electrically powered cars. The reasons are evident: power, speed, convenience, and cost. Gasoline-powered cars can go from 0 to 60 miles per hour in 6 seconds or less. They can go 200 miles between refills. EVs accelerate more slowly—a big disadvantage on the highway. Most go between 50 and 100 miles between charges. Their top speeds are still lower than those of cars with gasoline engines; however, they are getting faster. Some test vehicles have been clocked at up to 183 miles per hour. Finally, the cost of battery-pack replacements for EVs is quite high.

At the present time, electric cars are more expensive to operate than gasoline-powered cars are, but over time the costs will level out. Fuel costs for battery-powered cars, experts predict, will be 1 or 2 cents a mile. Fuel costs for gasoline-powered engines range from 5 to 10 cents a mile. In addition, EVs don't need transmissions, motor oil, or tune-ups.

When you get your license and start driving, you'll still go to the gas station and say, "Fill it up!" But who knows—by the time your own son or daughter starts to drive, the order may be, "Plug it in!" □

Putting the Wind to Work

AP/WIDE WORLD PHOTOS

Winds from Hurricane Roxanne lash Sanchez, Mexico

The power of wind can be a popular topic—especially when hurricane season rolls around or a tornado levels a town in the Midwest.

An early windmill. Windmills like this one used the power of the wind to rotate huge grindstones that crushed grain brought from local farms.

But the force of winds can be put to good use as well. For thousands of years, people have put the wind to work—to move boats, pump water, and grind grain.

Down on the Farm

Wind power can also be harnessed to generate electricity—if you choose the right location. That's where wind parks enter the picture. A wind park, or wind farm, is a large group of windmills built in a single area. Wind parks are usually erected in large, flat, open spaces, because hills, mountains, tall trees, or buildings block winds.

The largest wind farm in the United States covers 54 acres and contains 7500 windmills. It is located near San Francisco. This wind farm

Wind farms need large, open spaces. So do cows!

A close-up view of a modern windmill. The force of the wind turns the blades and rotates the vertical shaft that transfers the wind power to an electric generator.

was built in 1981. It has generated billions of kilowatt-hours of electricity.

Wind parks have also been built in many other countries. A wind park in Wales provides electricity to 20,000 homes. Wind power supplies 5 percent of the electricity in Denmark.

Transforming Energy

You can think of wind power as a form of solar energy. The sun warms the earth's atmosphere unevenly, causing air to move, swirl, and create wind. A wind turbine, perched at the top of each modern-day windmill, captures the wind. Most modern wind turbines have three large blades—sometimes more than 15 meters long.

Some windmills are as high as a 10- or 20-story building. Winds are stronger at higher levels than at lower ones. Therefore, tall windmills harness powerful gusts that are swirling above the earth's surface. Small windmills capture a gentle breeze.

All windmills work the same way. The blades rotate like a propeller when wind blows on them. The blades are connected to a hub that turns a shaft. The shaft runs into a generator, which converts mechanical energy to electrical energy. Electrical current then flows from the generator through the power lines of the local electric company and carries the energy to the user.

Putting the wind to work is a good idea for several reasons. It is environment-friendly. No pollution! It is inexpensive. And wind is a renewable resource. *You* may worry about "running out of wind," but nature never will! □

Introduction to Forces

Having fun on a trampoline. What forces are at work?

INTRODUCTION

Take a look at the photographs on this page. What forces are at work and what are they like? This is the first of several lessons in which you will investigate different forces. In this lesson, you will investigate two forces—the force of a rubber band and the force of gravity—and learn something about the nature of each. In Lessons 6 and 7, you will investigate the nature of friction and the forces that motors exert.

Preparing for a dive. What forces are at work?

OBJECTIVES FOR THIS LESSON

Describe the nature of forces and how they act on objects.

Determine the relationship between elastic force and the stretch of a rubber band.

Measure the weight of objects with different masses.

Describe how mass and weight (force of gravity) are related.

Use data tables and graphs to interpret data.

Getting Started

1. In your science notebook, write what you know or think you know about forces. List some forces that are familiar to you.

2. Share your ideas about forces and your list of forces with the class.

3. In this lesson, you will use a spring scale to measure forces. Before using the spring scale, make sure it is set properly. When there is no force on the scale, it should register zero. Lay the spring scale on the table and make sure it registers zero. If it does not, your teacher will show you how to adjust the scale.

4. Examine the spring scale and write answers to the following questions in your science notebook:

   A. *What happens to the reading on the scale when you pull horizontally on the scale?*

   B. *What are the units of measure for force on your scale?*

   C. *What is the maximum force that your scale can measure?*

   D. *How much force do the smaller marks along the scale represent?*

MATERIALS FOR
LESSON 5

For you
 1 copy of Student Sheet 5.1: What Is the Elastic Force of the Rubber Band?

For you and your lab partner
 1 pegboard assembly
 1 0- to 10-N spring scale
 1 large paper clip
 1 rubber band
 1 machine screw with wing nut
 1 meterstick
 5 large washers
 1 piece of masking tape

Inquiry 5.1
Measuring Elastic Force

PROCEDURE

1. In this inquiry, you will investigate the elastic force needed to stretch a rubber band. To set up the experiment, use a wing nut to fasten a machine screw to a corner of the pegboard assembly. Lay the pegboard assembly on its back on the table with the base projecting over the table's edge, as shown in Figure 5.1. Tape the board down as shown.

Figure 5.2 *With your finger, pull and stretch the rubber band.*

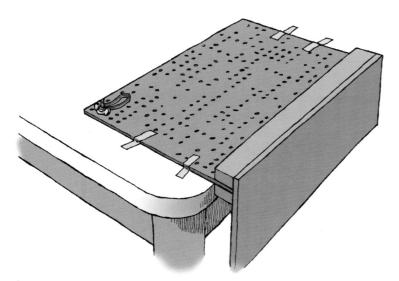

Figure 5.1 *Setup for pegboard assembly, machine screw, wing nut, and rubber band*

2. Put a rubber band around the screw. Leave enough room so that you can easily pull on the rubber band. With your finger, carefully stretch the rubber band far enough to feel the force of the pull (see Figure 5.2). When you stretch the rubber band, what do you feel and in what direction does the rubber band pull your finger?

3. Pull a little harder on the rubber band. Now what happens to it? Record your observations in your science notebook.

4. Hook the free end of the rubber band to the spring scale. It should be straight but not stretched, as shown in Figure 5.3.

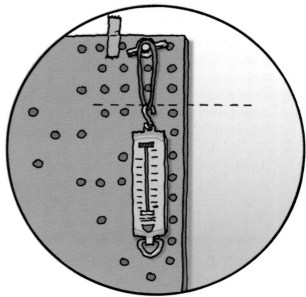

Figure 5.3 *The rubber band with the spring scale attached*

5. Tape the meterstick to the table so the zero mark on the meterstick is even with the end of the rubber band hooked to the spring scale (see Figure 5.4).

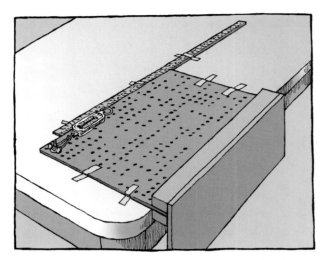

Figure 5.4 *Pegboard and rubber band set up with the meterstick*

6. Pull slowly on the spring scale until the rubber band is stretched 2.0 cm. Record the spring scale's force reading in Table 1 on Student Sheet 5.1: What Is the Elastic Force of the Rubber Band?

7. Stretch the rubber band another 2.0 cm and record the force. Repeat this process for each 2.0-cm interval shown in the data table. Each time you stretch the rubber band, record the force on the spring scale.

8. Look at the measurements in your data table and answer Question 1 on Student Sheet 5.1: What happens to the force required to stretch the rubber band when the stretching distance is doubled? Review at least three instances of doubling the distance.

9. Use the data you collected to make a graph. Remember to plot the dependent variable versus the independent variable. Make sure both axes are uniformly scaled and properly labeled. Give your graph a title.

10. Use your graph to answer Questions 2, 3, and 4 on the student sheet: What does your graph tell you about the relationship between the force needed to stretch the rubber band and the distance it stretches? Did the force needed to stretch the rubber band increase by the same amount each time you stretched the rubber band another 2.0 cm? Is the answer visible in the graph? Can you predict the force needed to stretch the rubber band to 40.0 cm? Why or why not?

11. Discuss your findings with the class.

THE DIFFERENCE BETWEEN MASS AND WEIGHT

How much do you weigh? What is your mass? Many people think that these two questions are asking the same thing. But that's not true. Weight and mass are different. Although many people know what their weight is, few know their mass.

Weight is a measure of the force of gravity pulling on a body. If you weigh 400 newtons (90 pounds), then gravity pulls your body down toward the earth with a force of 400 newtons. You can measure your weight by standing on a bathroom scale. When you stand on the scale, your body's weight compresses the spring in the scale. The amount the spring is compressed is proportional to your body's weight. If you went to the moon, you would weigh less because the force of gravity on the moon's surface is not as strong as the force of gravity on the surface of the earth. In fact, on the moon, you would weigh only one-sixth as much as on the earth.

Now what about your mass? Mass is a measure of how much matter is in your body. The mass of a person who weights 400 newtons on the earth is about 40 kilograms. Mass is measured differently from weight. Mass is measured in kilograms. You can measure your mass by sitting on a balance. You sit on one side of the balance and put objects whose masses are known on the other side. When the sum of the known masses equals your mass, the system balances. Suppose you went to the moon. Would your mass change? The answer is no—the matter in your body would be the same as it is on the earth. If you do not add to or take away any matter from your body, your mass stays the same, no matter where you are.

Inquiry 5.2
Measuring Gravitational Force

PROCEDURE

1. In this inquiry, you will investigate the force of gravity on various objects. Before beginning, read about the difference between "mass" and "weight."

2. Your teacher will give you some objects with different masses to study. Pick up each object and describe its weight. List the objects in order, from heaviest to lightest. Which objects are heaviest? Record the list in your science notebook. Discuss your list with the class.

3. Think about the statement "Different objects have different weights." Develop a hypothesis about the relationship between weight and mass.

4. With the rest of the class, develop a plan that uses spring scales and washers to investigate the relationship between the weight of an object and its mass. Record the procedure in your science notebook.

5. Work with your partner to carry out your procedure. Remember to do the following:

A. Make a table in your notebook to record your data.

B. Describe how you will measure mass.

C. Develop a plan to analyze your data.

D. Hold the scale vertically, and make sure it registers zero when nothing is hanging on the hook.

6. After collecting and analyzing your data, compare your results with the results of other groups and discuss them with the class.

7. In your notebook, summarize what you learned about weight in this inquiry. Give evidence to support your conclusion.

REFLECTING ON WHAT YOU'VE DONE

1. In your notebook, write the answers to the questions in Steps 2 through 6 below. Discuss your answers with the class.

2. *Use the results of your experiment with the rubber band to answer the following questions:*

A. You want to pull a cart along the floor. How would you use the rubber band to do this?

B. Suppose you want to apply a force twice as big as the one you would use for Question 2A. What would you do to the rubber band to produce twice as much force?

3. *Use the results of your weight experiment to answer the following questions:*

A. What is the mass of a single washer?

B. What is the weight of a single washer?

C. When you added more washers (mass) to the spring scale, what did the spring do?

D. What do you call the force that makes objects have weight?

E. In what direction does this force pull on the washers?

4. *From your observations, explain why different objects have different weights. What do you think determines the weight of an object? Support your answer with data.*

5. *In this inquiry you examined forces that pull on objects. Give an example of another way to exert a force on an object.*

6. *In your science notebook, define "force."*

BUNGEE JUMPING:
The Forces Are With You

Bungee jumping isn't for wimps! You leap from a bridge or high platform and drop like a rock for hundreds of feet. And just when you're thinking that you'll never stop falling, you do. You stop just short of hitting the ground. What saved you? You may think it's the thin elastic cord around your ankles. You just experienced two powerful forces—gravity and elastic force.

Real Swingers!

You might think that bungee jumping is as new as the closest amusement park, but actually it's been around for centuries. In a village called Bunlap on Pentecost Island in the South Pacific Ocean, it is an annual ritual. The islanders call it land diving.

Each year at harvest time, the men of the village erect towers made of tree trunks, branches,

A bungee jumper takes the plunge off a bridge over the Nanaimo River in Canada. Gravity and elastic force work together in this thrilling sport.

and vines. These towers are 15 to 25 meters high. Then each man selects some of the same vines to make his own bungee cord. One after another, the men and older boys take their homemade bungee cords and climb the tower. The younger jumpers climb only part of the way, but the older men go to the very top. Before the jump, friends tie a vine to each of the jumper's legs. They anchor the other end to the tower.

The jumper takes his position. Below, the villagers sing and dance. He raises his arm, and the crowd becomes silent. The jumper plunges to earth. If all goes as planned, the springy, elastic vines break his fall just before he reaches the ground. Fellow members of the tribe rush to untie the vines and begin to dance in his honor.

Both men and boys on Pentecost Island participate in land diving. They tie bungee cords made from springy liana vines around their ankles and leap from the top of towers 25 meters high.

Jumping Across Continents

Bungee jumping became popular in the western world in 1979, when members of the Dangerous Sports Club at Oxford University, who had read about the land divers of Pentecost Island, leaped from the 75-meter-high Clifton Bridge in the city of Bristol, England. Because it was an important occasion, they were all wearing tuxedos and top hats! Later, these men traveled around the world. They leaped from the Golden Gate Bridge in California and the Royal Gorge in Colorado.

As soon as people heard of this thrilling new sport, many wanted to try it for themselves. Soon they were lining up at amusement parks and paying for the privilege of taking a death-defying leap.

There's Science Behind It

Suppose you want to make a jump. How would you convince your mom or dad that it's really not dangerous?

You'd tell them that when you're bungee jumping, the forces are with you—the force of gravity and elastic force, that is.

Let's take an imaginary jump and see what happens.

First, the operator hooks you up to a bungee cord—a stretchy, elastic material. After a few instructions, you're ready to leap. You close your eyes and step off into thin air. You immediately feel the pull of gravity.

You open your eyes. The ground is rushing toward you like a railroad train. As you near the

AP/WIDE WORLD PHOTOS

A diver takes the plunge at an amusement-park bungee-jump ride.

ground, the bungee cord stretches like a gigantic rubber band. The more the cord stretches, the stronger its force becomes.

Finally, you reach the point where the upward pull of the cord is greater than the downward pull of gravity. You feel an upward pull ("Thank you, elastic force!") Your fall slows then stops—inches above the ground. ("Thank you, thank you!")

It's not over yet. The upward pull of the cord, now stronger than gravity, slings you back into the air. You fall again. Rise, and fall, rise and fall—you feel like a fish at the end of a line!

Each time, the movement becomes less extreme. You don't even notice by now. What matters is that you *survived*.

And if the line is not too long, you'll have time for one more jump before the park closes! □

QUESTIONS

1. Where did bungee jumping originate?
2. Why does a bungee jumper fall?
3. What keeps the jumper from hitting the ground?

HOOKE AND NEWTON:
Geniuses at Work

Cooperation pays off in science, but competition also has its rewards. Two of the leading scientists of 17th-century England, Sir Isaac Newton and Robert Hooke, were rivals almost all their lives. Each made important contributions to physics. Robert Hooke discovered the nature of elastic force, and Sir Isaac Newton investigated light. The nature of gravity was a subject that fascinated both men, but they also had many other scientific interests.

Hooke studied his world in many ways—through a telescope as well as through a microscope. With the microscope, which he built himself, Hooke looked at fish scales, feathers, and cork. He noted that these objects, viewed under magnification, were made up of tiny compartments. He named these compartments "cells." Hooke published a book entitled *Micrographica* that contained many beautiful drawings of the things he'd seen with his microscope.

Hooke's investigations of forces resulted in Hooke's Law, which states that the force a spring exerts depends on how far it is stretched.

Sir Isaac Newton

Although Hooke made many fine drawings of things he saw, no known portrait of him exists.

These may look like flowers in a field, but they are actually mold spores as seen through Hooke's microscope.

Under the Apple Tree

Meanwhile, unknown to Hooke, Isaac Newton had an unexpected opportunity to work on the problem of gravity. Newton, who was a college professor, had some free time when the bubonic plague caused universities across England to close. In 1666, he returned to the farm where he had grown up.

One day he was sitting outside under a tree, thinking serious thoughts—in this case, about why the moon orbits the earth. Suddenly, an apple plopped to the ground.

Newton's eyes lit up. A hypothesis! Perhaps gravity, the force that pulled the apple to the ground, was the same force that keeps the moon and the planets in orbit. In other words, the same force that had long been known to operate on the earth was holding the solar system together. Earth and the heavens might operate according to the same physical principles! He did some mathematical calculations and became convinced that his hypothesis was correct: Gravity holds the moon in its orbit as it revolves around the earth.

But Newton did not publish his findings. Time passed.

Twenty years later, other scientists were still trying to understand the force of gravity and explain what keeps the planets in their orbits. Among them was Hooke. By this time Hooke and Newton, both famous for other discoveries, were also well known because of the rivalry that had grown up between them. Hooke had publicly criticized some of Newton's theories about light.

A third scientist, Edmund Halley, was a friend of both men. Probably feeling very proud of himself, Halley asked Newton whether he understood how gravity keeps an object in orbit. "Of course," Newton probably replied, "I figured it out 20 years ago."

"Well," Halley might have responded, "you'd better watch out, because Robert Hooke is pretty close to figuring it out, too."

Newton decided it was time to publish his findings on gravity. The result was a book that would become famous around the world: *Mathematical Principles of Natural Philosophy*. In it, he described how gravity works and demonstrated that objects on earth operate under the same principles as objects in space. The book also contains Newton's three laws of motion.

Sir Isaac may have beat Hooke in figuring out how gravity works, but both men made important discoveries and wrote books that have influenced science for centuries. Many people regard them as two of the greatest scientists of the 17th century. ☐

An apple falling from a tree inspired Newton to solve the mystery of how gravity works.

6
The Force of Friction

What force stops the baseball player as he slides into third base?

INTRODUCTION

In Lesson 5, you investigated the properties of gravity and elastic forces in a rubber band. In this lesson, you will explore another force—friction. Friction is a force you experience every day. People spend time, money, and effort to reduce it. You might be surprised to learn that friction is not always bad. It can be very helpful.

You will investigate the force of friction as you pull a wooden block at a constant speed across a surface. As you do so, you will investigate three variables—surface type, weight (load), and surface area (base area)—and determine how each affects the frictional force between the block and the surface. In each trial, you will change one variable and keep the other two the same. This method is an example of good experimental design. As in the previous inquiries, you will record observations, collect data, and draw conclusions based on what you discover about friction. Understanding friction will help you understand motion, which you will study later in this module.

OBJECTIVES FOR THIS LESSON

Observe the properties of sliding friction.

Measure the force of friction on a wooden block pulled across different surfaces.

Measure the force of friction on loads of different weights.

Measure the force of friction on a wooden block with different base areas in contact with a surface.

Getting Started

1. Discuss what you know about friction with your lab partner and then with the rest of the class.

2. Identify a situation in which friction works against you. Then identify one in which friction works for you. Think of situations where friction is very low or almost zero. What would happen if there were no friction at all?

3. Your teacher will share information with you about how to use the spring scales to measure the force of friction. Listen carefully and ask questions if you are not sure how to make the measurements.

MATERIALS FOR LESSON 6

For you
1 copy of Student Sheet 6.1: What a Drag!
1 copy of Student Sheet 6.2: Changing the Load

For you and your lab partner
2 wooden blocks with attached screw hook
1 0- to 2.5-N spring scale
1 0- to 10-N spring scale
1 piece of waxed paper
1 piece of paper towel
1 piece of fine sandpaper
1 piece of coarse sandpaper
1 meterstick
1 rubber band
1 piece of masking tape

Inquiry 6.1
Pulling a Block Across Different Surfaces

PROCEDURE

1. Lay the spring scales on the tabletop. Does the pointer register zero? If not, adjust it to read zero.

2. In this inquiry, you will investigate the force of friction on a block as you pull it across each of the following surfaces: the plain tabletop, waxed paper, a paper towel, fine sandpaper, and coarse sandpaper. Tape the four surface strips (waxed paper, paper towel, fine sandpaper, coarse sandpaper) to the tabletop. Measure and mark off another 27-cm length on the bare tabletop.

3. You will need to decide which spring scale to use for your measurements. If you are not sure which to use, try making some measurements of the forces needed to pull the block using the scale. The best scale to use is one that will register the force to pull the block, yet not go off scale when you exert the maximum force needed to pull the block.

4. Attach the hook on the spring scale to the round screw hook on the wooden block, as shown in Figure 6.1.

5. How do you think the frictional force on the block will compare as you pull the block across the different surfaces? Write your prediction in your science notebook.

6. Before you start to collect data, practice by pulling the wooden block with the spring scale across a surface at a steady rate, as shown in Figure 6.2. Make sure you hold the spring scale parallel to the tabletop and pull horizontally on the block. As you move the block at a steady speed, observe the force reading. You will probably find that the force is not perfectly steady. When the spring scale reading is not steady, it is best to do several trials and average your results. How many trials should you do for each surface? Discuss this with your partner and decide on the number of trials needed in order to obtain accurate force data.

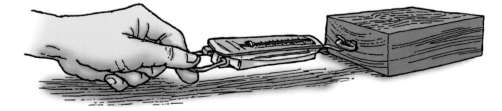

Figure 6.1 *Wooden block connected to a spring scale*

Figure 6.2 *Pulling a wooden block across a surface to measure the force of friction*

7. Pull the block across each of the five surfaces and collect force data for each surface. Be sure to pull the block across the entire length of the surface. Record your data in Table 1 on Student Sheet 6.1: What a Drag! Calculate the average force for each surface.

8. How can you graphically represent the average force data for each surface? What kind of graph should you use? Construct a graph on Student Sheet 6.1.

9. In your science notebook, record your answers to the following questions:

A. Which surface required the greatest force to pull the wooden block across it?

B. Which surface required the least force?

C. Did the weight of your wooden block change as the surfaces changed?

D. Review the variables for this lesson. Which variables did not change as you tested each surface?

10. Be prepared to discuss your answers to the questions in Step 9 with the class.

Inquiry 6.2
Changing the Load

PROCEDURE

1. Think about and discuss with your lab partner the following question: What will happen to the effort force needed to pull the block if you change the weight of the block? Write your prediction in your science notebook.

2. This inquiry requires that you and your lab partner work as a team and collaborate with the other teams in your class. Each team should collect data. But there is not enough time for each individual team to check all surfaces with different loads. Therefore, you will need to work together as a class and assign different surfaces to different teams. Each surface needs to be assigned to at least two teams.

3. Design a data table on Student Sheet 6.2: Changing the Load to record your measurements. Discuss with the class how you will measure the weight of the load in each trial.

4. Change the weight of the load by stacking more blocks, one at a time, on the original block. Each time you add a block, measure the force it takes to pull this load at a steady speed across the surface. Share blocks with another team so both teams can gather data for a load of up to four blocks.

5. Graph your data.

6. Compare your data and graph with that of a team that used the same surface. Discuss with your partner and the other team the relationship between the load (total weight of the block or blocks) and the frictional force. Record the description in your science notebook.

7. Compare your data with the data of groups that used different surfaces. What do you find? Record your findings in your science notebook.

8. Think about the variables in this investigation. What did you keep constant as you changed the weight of the blocks? Record your answer in your science notebook.

9. Share your results with the class.

Inquiry 6.3
Changing the Surface Area

PROCEDURE

1. Look at your block. You can turn the block on its wide side and pull on it, or stand it on one of its narrow sides and pull on it. When the block is on its wide side, the area in contact with the surface is greater than when it is on its narrow side. You pulled the block across the surfaces on its wide side in previous trials. Predict what will happen to the force of friction if you pull the block on a narrow side across the surface. Write your prediction in your science notebook.

2. Construct a data table in your notebook to record the description of each surface area of the block (wide or narrow) and the measurement of the force needed to pull the block at a steady rate across the surface (waxed paper, fine sandpaper, and so on). Different teams should use different surfaces. Make sure you record the surface you use. Be prepared to share the data you collect with the class. Your class should design a class data table on the board or on a transparency.

3. Put a rubber band around the block so that it is below the center (about one-fourth of the way to the top of the block as measured from the table). Attach the spring scale hook to the rubber band and pull the block so that it moves smoothly across the table, as shown in Figure 6.3. Measure the frictional force as the block slides at a constant speed along the surface. Do this for each side of the block.

Figure 6.3 *Attach a rubber band and a spring scale to the block as shown here to pull the block on one of its narrow sides.*

4. Record your data, and then discuss the results with your team and share your results with the class. Add your results to the class data table.

5. Answer the following question in your notebook: How did your prediction compare with the results?

6. Think about the variables. Which variables did you keep constant this time? Record your answer in your science notebook.

REFLECTING ON WHAT YOU'VE DONE
Write answers to the following questions in your science notebook:

A. What have you learned about friction in this lesson? In your science notebook, summarize in several paragraphs what you have learned about the force of friction. In your summary, include factors that affect frictional force and explain how you measure it.

B. In this lesson, you measured sliding friction. Why does the force on the spring scale measure the force of friction while the block moves at a steady speed?

C. Suppose you used ice as a surface for the block to slide on. What results would you get in this lab? Consider results for all three variables—surface type, weight of the block, and surface area.

NATURE PUTS ON THE BRAKES

Skydiving is a sport that many people enjoy. But it takes courage! When skydivers leap from planes, you might think that the constant pull of gravity would make them fall faster and faster until their parachutes opened and allowed them to glide safely back to the earth. But that's not quite what happens.

At the beginning of a skydive, a diver's fall does speed up or accelerate rapidly. But as the diver falls, the acceleration continually decreases until the diver stops speeding up. The diver then falls at a constant velocity. ("Velocity" is the speed at which an object is traveling in a single direction—in the case of a skydiver, down!) The constant velocity that the skydiver reaches is called terminal velocity. It usually takes a skydiver about 10 seconds to reach terminal velocity.

Forces on Skydivers

It is the forces on skydivers that make them eventually reach terminal velocity. To the

By controlling the amount of the body that is exposed to the drag of the air, a skydiver can change the terminal velocity. Here, a skydiver falls in a spread-eagle position. Since the maximum amount of body is exposed to the air, the air friction is greater and the terminal velocity is smaller than when the body is pointed straight down.

© BENELUX PRESS//FPG INTERNATIONAL/PNI

observer, gravity is the more obvious force. If gravity were the only force acting on skydivers, their velocity would continue to increase at a rate of 9.8 meters per second each second that they fall. Ten seconds into the fall, they would be moving at 98 meters per second if gravity were the only force on them. As they continued to fall, they would continue to go faster and faster.

But gravity isn't the only force on skydivers. Air friction, or drag, pushes up on their bodies as they fall through the air. ("Drag" is another word for the force of friction between the skydiver and the air.) The force of gravity is constant, but drag increases with the skydiver's speed. As skydivers fall, they eventually reach the point where the size of the drag force equals the size of the force of gravity. The drag continues to push up while gravity continues to pull down. But now, the two forces counterbalance each other. As a result, skydivers fall at a constant velocity—terminal velocity.

Controlling Terminal Velocity
Skydivers can make their terminal velocity faster or slower by changing *body position* as

Air Friction   Gravity

Terminal velocity is a result of the interaction of two forces: gravity and air friction (drag).

Because the terminal velocity of spread-eagle sky-divers is very nearly the same, they can form patterns like the one seen here as they fall.

AP/WIDE WORLD PHOTOS

Left: *Skydivers leaping from their plane*
Below: *Parachutes are designed to take advantage of air friction, allowing skydivers to land safely.*

they fall. For skydivers falling with their backs or stomachs parallel to the earth, terminal velocity is about 50 meters per second after 10 seconds. If skydivers were going head first, terminal velocity would reach twice that rate, or 100 meters per second.

Why the difference? Because terminal velocity also depends on the surface area of the diver against which the air pushes during the fall. The greater the surface area, the greater the drag. The smaller the surface area, the less the drag and the faster the fall. To understand the comparison, think of swimmers—they feel much more resistance entering the water with a belly flop than with a nosedive.

Falling at terminal velocity without a parachute is still too fast to land safely on the ground. So skydivers do need that parachute. Parachutes help slow skydivers even more by greatly increasing their surface area. Large parachutes are more powerful than small ones. The larger the parachute, the greater the air resistance acting on the diver, and the slower the terminal velocity. The probability of a smooth, safe landing increases proportionately! ☐

QUESTIONS

1. What forces act on a skydiver to make the diver reach terminal velocity?
2. How is air friction different from the sliding friction studied in this lesson?

Rock Climbing:
Two People, One Powerful Force

CORBIS/GALEN ROWELL

At a time like this, friction comes in handy.

Rock climbing is not usually thought of as a team sport. For most climbers, however, it is. The climber has a partner, called a belayer.

As the climber ascends the slope, the belayer often remains below. The job of the belayer is to keep the climber from falling. The climber or belayer places an anchor at the top of the climb or at some other convenient location. The belayer holds one end of a rope. The other end of the rope is threaded through the anchor and then attached to the climber's waist. As the climber ascends the slope, the belayer holds the rope. If the climber should slip and fall, the belayer would pull on the rope and prevent the climber from falling to the ground below.

Going Up!

Both partners make full use of a powerful force called friction. Climbers use friction to make their way up to the top. While ascending a steep rock face, the climbers constantly look for "holds"—cracks and crevices into which they can wedge their feet, or small rocks or ledges that they can grasp or step on. If the rock face is smooth, climbers have to rely only on the friction between their hands and feet and the rock face to keep from falling.

Climbers also increase the force of friction by wearing shoes with specially designed soles. These soles cover more of the foot than the soles of everyday shoes do. This makes it easier for the climber to get some part of the sole of the shoe on the rock. This is important because the soles are designed to create a lot of friction with the rock.

Climbers' shoes are designed to grip the rock surface and to prevent their feet from slipping.

Holding On!

While climbers make their way up the mountain or cliff, belayers keep an eye on their progress. Belayers use one of several methods to increase the friction on the rope and ensure that the climbers will be safe. For example, belayers can wrap the rope around their hips. The friction between their clothing and the rope wrapped around them is far greater than the friction between their hands and the ropes. Should the climbers slip, belayers can control the fall better than they could if the rope were just in their hands. More often belayers thread the rope around special metal devices that increase the friction on the rope and decrease the force the belayer must exert if the climber falls.

Climbers and belayers aren't usually thinking about friction when they're moving up a mountainside. They're focusing on their goal: reaching the top. Friction helps keep them safer and makes the climb easier. And, unlike those special shoes and mountaineering equipment, it's absolutely free! □

Belaying devices for climbing

Climbers prepare their gear.

The Force Exerted by a Motor

The word "motor" comes from a Latin word that means "to move." Motors are used to lift and move heavy loads, like this huge metal drum.

INTRODUCTION

Motors are all around you. These devices generate motion by turning other forms of energy into mechanical energy. Motors do work and make difficult tasks easier. They range in size from tiny to huge. Later in the lesson, you will read about some of these motors. You will also use batteries to run a small electric motor, and you will investigate the motor's ability to lift a load of washers.

OBJECTIVES FOR THIS LESSON

Design and execute an experiment to determine the operating conditions that produce the maximum force from a motor.

Analyze experimental data.

Write a conclusion based on experimental evidence.

Measure the force that a motor exerts under the best operating conditions.

Getting Started

1. With the class, discuss the elements of a well-designed experiment. Review the meaning of independent and dependent variables.

2. Your teacher has displayed a model of an apparatus used in this inquiry. Identify each part and what each part does.

3. Discuss with your partner and then with the class the following questions:

   A. How many washers can the motor lift?

   B. Can you think of anything that would affect the motor's ability to lift the load of washers? If so, what is it?

4. Record a summary of the class ideas in your science notebook.

MATERIALS FOR LESSON 7

For you and your lab partner

1 electric motor with wire leads and alligator clips
1 motor pulley with nail
1 motor clamp
1 knife switch
1 pegboard assembly
3 machine screws with wing nuts
3 D-cell batteries
3 D-cell battery holders
5 insulated connector wires with alligator clips
1 large paper clip
1 piece of string
1 piece of masking tape
8 large washers
1 0- to 10-N spring scale

Inquiry 7.1
Measuring the Force Exerted by a Motor

PROCEDURE FOR PERIOD 1

1. Examine the equipment at your lab station. Predict what arrangement of motor, batteries, and string will enable the motor to lift the largest number of washers. Record your prediction in your science notebook.

2. Your goals for this period are to set up and test your equipment and to plan a procedure to test your prediction. Set up the motor, knife switch, and pegboard assembly as shown in Figure 7.1. If your teacher has not already done so, remove the black caps from the screw terminals on the knife switch and return the caps to your teacher. Use two screws and wing nuts to attach the motor clamp to the pegboard; fasten the knife switch to the pegboard using one screw and wing nut.

3. Compare your setup with the model setup to make sure everything is correctly connected.

4. Attach one battery to the motor and make sure the motor works. If it doesn't, check the connections. If the setup still won't work, ask your teacher for help.

5. Think about the following questions:

   A. *Do you think the number of batteries you connect to the motor will have an effect on the motor performance?*

   B. *If you use more than one battery, do you think the way the batteries are connected will matter?* (Figure 7.2 shows different battery arrangements.)

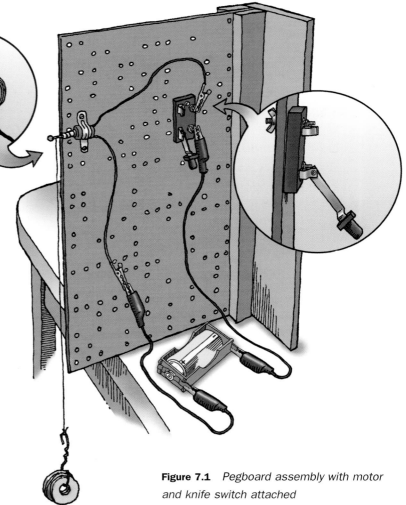

Figure 7.1 *Pegboard assembly with motor and knife switch attached*

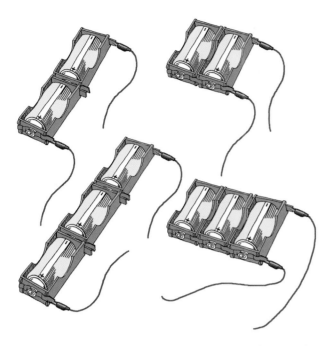

Figure 7.2 *Some possible ways to connect the batteries*

9. Design an experiment that shows the effect of each independent variable on the total number of washers the motor can lift. Remember, when you conduct a scientific investigation, change one variable at a time while keeping all the others constant.

10. In your notebook, write a procedure that describes which variable you will change and how you will change it. Do this for each independent variable.

11. Design a table (or tables) in your science notebook to record your data. You will use this table to share results with the class.

6. There are two ways to connect the string to the motor. Figure 7.3 shows both arrangements. Do you think it matters if you wind the string around the plastic pulley instead of around the nail?

7. Record the independent variables for this experiment in your science notebook.

8. List the dependent variable in your science notebook.

Figure 7.3 *Two ways to connect the string to the motor pulley with nail*

SAFETY TIPS

When connecting two or more batteries in series, always connect them in a single line with the positive terminal of one battery connected to the negative terminal of the next battery.

When connecting two or more batteries in parallel, the positive terminal of one battery is connected to the positive terminal of the next battery, and the negative terminal of one battery is connected to the negative terminal of the next battery.

Connecting battery terminals in other configurations can create a short circuit and may cause the battery and battery holder to become very hot or even create a fire.

PROCEDURE FOR PERIOD 2

1. Conduct the experiment following the procedure you designed. Record your observations and data in your science notebook.

2. Use the results of your experiment to describe the arrangement of motor, batteries, and string that allows the motor to lift the greatest number of washers. Describe the arrangement in your science notebook or draw a picture showing the arrangement.

3. Using a spring scale, measure the force of the motor for this arrangement. To measure the pull of the motor, follow these directions:

A. Set up your pegboard as shown in Figure 7.4.

B. Make a loop in the loose end of the string and attach it to the spring-scale hook.

C. Secure the other end of the spring scale with a machine screw and wing nut so it is positioned as shown in Figure 7.4.

D. Fasten the string to the motor, using the arrangement that allows the motor to lift the greatest number of washers.

E. Close the knife switch and observe the force reading on the spring scale. Record the reading in your table, and then open the knife switch.

F. If you have time, repeat the experiment several times and record the measurements to show that your data are reproducible (that is, you get the same or similar results each time you do the experiment). If you collect several sets of data, average the data and record this average value in your notebook.

4. When you finish your experiment, clean up and store the materials as your teacher directs.

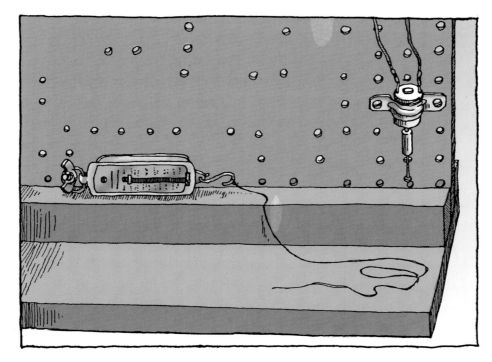

Figure 7.4 *Setup for measuring the motor's force*

PROCEDURE FOR PERIOD 3

1. Review your data and observations and discuss the results of your experiment with your lab partner.

2. Discuss the following questions with the class:

A. What are the effects of changing the following variables:

    i. number of batteries
    ii. series versus parallel connections of the batteries
    iii. winding the string around the plastic pulley instead of around the nail

B. What might account for the variations in the number of washers lifted by a given motor?

REFLECTING ON WHAT YOU'VE DONE

1. Write a conclusion summarizing what you learned. Record your final observations and conclusions, including the following:

A. Your observations of the effect on the motor of changing the number of batteries connected to the motor

B. The effect you observed when connecting the batteries to the motor in series and in parallel

C. Any differences you observed in the motor's performance between when the string was wound around the nail and when it was wound around the plastic pulley

D. A detailed description of the setup that allowed the motor to lift the greatest number of washers, along with any drawings you wish to include

2. Answer this question in your science notebook:

What is the maximum force exerted by the motor?

MOTORS—
Getting Smaller Every Day

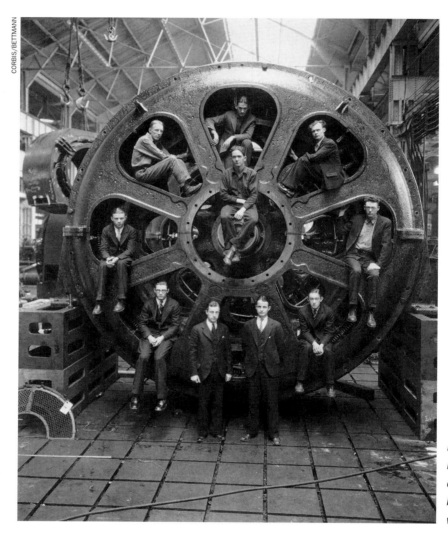

Motors come in many sizes. What do you think this big electric motor was used for?

You get up in the morning and shower, then blow-dry your hair and brush your teeth. You take some orange juice out of the refrigerator and get a piece of toast. You've been up for only about half an hour, and you've already used at least three appliances with motors.

Of course, if you'd been born 200 years ago, your life would have been quite different. Before electric motors were invented, humans had to rely on their own muscle power, or on the muscle power of animals, to do most of their work. They captured the power of the wind or of falling water to grind grain.

But in the early 1800s, scientists discovered the relationship between electricity and magnetism. This led to the invention of electric motors. The electric motor changed the course of everyday life, and that change continues.

Magnets and Motors

In 1820, Hans Oersted, a professor in Copenhagen, Denmark, discovered the link between electricity and magnetism. Oersted connected a copper wire to a large copper–zinc battery. An electrical current flowed through the wire. Oersted then noticed that when he brought a magnetic compass near the current-carrying wire, the needle of the compass moved. He concluded that the electrical current created a magnetic field.

Oersted's discovery was the basis of additional research by the French scientist André Ampère, who developed a theory to explain the connection between electricity and magnetism. Then, in 1821, Michael Faraday repeated Oersted's experiment and built the first electric motor. To do this, Faraday used the magnetic force that caused the compass needle to move and put it to work.

Faraday's motor was small and simple. It consisted of a battery, a spool of wire, and a bar magnet. When Faraday ran an electric current through the wire, the magnet rotated. Inventors who followed would apply this principle to move the shaft of larger and larger electric motors.

even be seen by the unaided eye. They are called micromotors, or micromachines. You might say they come in two sizes: small and supersmall.

The small motors are the product of microtechnology, which measures things in microns. (A micron is one-millionth of a meter.) Just how small are they? Hundreds of thousands of microdevices could sit on the surface of a piece of toast.

Supersmall motors are the product of a new science called nanotechnology ("nano" means "one-billionth"). Scientists in this exciting field are trying to build devices on the atomic or molecular scale. Micromotors of this size could be used to work on individual cells in the human body.

About 600 research labs around the world are doing work on micromotors, and many U.S. companies have begun to develop commercial applications for them. Interest in these motors is high, because once the designs are perfected, the machines will not be expensive or hard to make. Making them will involve the same procedures that engineers already use to manufacture microchips for computers.

Smaller Is Better

Although "Bigger Is Better" might have been the motto of inventors and designers who followed Faraday, many of today's most interesting motors can't

Sometimes a tiny motor is just what you need. This is a picture of the world's smallest remote-controlled model gliding plane. It is 109 millimeters long and has a wing span of 75 millimeters. The mass of the plane, with its motor and microbattery, is only 0.97 gram.

AP/WIDE WORLD PHOTOS

Microsensors and micromotors can be put inside small probes. The Personal Satellite Assistant shown here is only the size of a softball. It will carry sensors to monitor the amount of oxygen and carbon dioxide in a spacecraft, as well as monitor bacteria growth, air temperature, and air pressure. It also contains a video camera and its own propulsion system.

AP/WIDE WORLD PHOTOS

What will these small machines be used for? One company has designed a microsensor that can trigger an air bag in a car to deploy. Micromachines can shoot out the ink in ink-jet printers and regulate the mixture of gasoline and air in automobiles. Designers are talking about microgyroscopes that could keep cars from skidding or keep hikers from getting lost in the woods. Wristwatch-sized radios are in the planning stages.

Meteorologists can send microweather stations (about the size of a quarter) to other planets to measure temperature, density, and pressure in their atmospheres. Meanwhile, back on planet Earth, chemical engineers are designing a "microplane" that will fly through the ventilation systems to monitor the air quality in buildings.

Micromotors will have many uses in medicine. Today, microsensors are already being used to monitor blood pressure in people who have had

This may look big, but it is actually the first magnetic micromotor made with nickel. It was developed by Professor Henry Guckel at the Wisconsin Center for Applied Microelectronics and Micromotors.

© 1991 UW-MADISON

035000 20KV X120 250um

heart attacks. Biomedical engineers foresee using miniature motors to remove plaque from inside the arteries of people who are at risk for heart disease. Tiny gears no wider than a human hair could be used to send microrobots into the blood-stream to perform surgical repairs. Also in devel-opment is the "thermometer pill." Less than 2 centimeters long, this capsule is filled with micro-circuits. It moves through the digestive tract and sends information to a computer, which analyzes the data that doctors can use to make diagnoses.

What other uses do you see for micromotors? How might they work? What would they look like? What would you name them? ☐

Work and the Motor

Are the cyclists in this picture doing work?

CORBIS/ANNIE GRIFFITHS BELT

INTRODUCTION

To most people, work is the physical or mental effort it takes to get something done. If you ask a scientist, work takes a little more time to explain. In this lesson, you will learn and use the scientific definition of work and learn how to calculate work.

You will make a number of measurements to use in calculating work. Calculating is important in science. This lesson will require you to use your math skills. Good science combines facts and figures. Mathematics is a great tool of science because it helps to describe how things behave and it helps scientists predict how some objects or processes will behave in the future. Italian astronomer Galileo and English physicist and mathematician Sir Isaac Newton were among the first to realize the combined power of math and science.

OBJECTIVES FOR THIS LESSON

Define "work."

Describe the units of measure for work.

Use force and distance measurements to calculate work.

Compare the work done by different forces.

Compare the force exerted by a motor that is connected to three batteries in series with the force needed to lift a small sled.

In Lessons 5, 6, and 7, you studied four different forces and learned something about how each force behaves. Those forces have different properties, but they also have something in common—they can all do work. In this lesson, you will learn how forces do work and how to calculate the amount of work being done. You will calculate the work done by three of the forces you studied—gravity, motors, and friction.

Getting Started

1. In your group, discuss the meaning of the word "work." List examples of work being done. Share examples with the class.

2. Read "The Meaning of Work" in this lesson. When you finish, review the examples of work you listed earlier. Do your examples match the scientific meaning of work? Discuss this with the class.

3. With the class, review how to calculate a value for work and explain the units of measure for work.

4. Work out this problem: Alice pulls a sled with a force of 12 N. She pulls the sled through a distance of 5 m. How much work does Alice do on the sled? In your notebook, write down your calculation and check your answer. Keep this sample as a reference for when it is time to calculate work.

MATERIALS FOR LESSON 8

For you

- Your completed copy of Student Sheet 6.1: What a Drag!
- 1 copy of Student Sheet 8.1a: How Much Work Was Done?
- 1 copy of Student Sheet 8.2: Lifting a Load

For your group

- 1 electric motor with wire leads and alligator clips
- 1 motor pulley with nail
- 1 motor clamp
- 1 knife switch
- 1 pegboard assembly
- 3 machine screws with wing nuts
- 3 D-cell batteries
- 3 D-cell battery holders
- 5 insulated connector wires with alligator clips
- 1 large paper clip
- 1 piece of string
- 1 piece of masking tape
- 14 large washers, 30 g
- 1 0- to 10-N spring scale
- 1 meterstick
  K'NEX® parts for sled (see Appendix A: Directory of K'NEX® Parts):
  - 1 orange connector (C3)
  - 14 red connectors (C4)
  - 8 yellow connectors (C10)
  - 8 green rods (R1)
  - 4 white rods (R2)
  - 3 blue rods (R3)
  - 4 red rods (R6)

THE MEANING OF WORK

It isn't hard to understand what most people mean when they talk about work—

"I'm going to work."

"This job is hard work."

"I worked hard to study for this test."

In everyday speech, the word "work" refers to the effort it takes to get things done. Manual labor is seen as work; so is mental labor.

But in science, "work" has a narrow definition. Work is done on an object, a scientist would say, when a force acts on an object and it moves some distance. To calculate the work done on an object, the force that pushes or pulls on the object is multiplied by the distance the object moves. Work involves both force and distance.

Activities that may seem like work to you might *not* seem like work to a scientist. For example, if you sit quietly and study for a long time, a scientist would say that you're not doing any work at all! And you could push against a car until you were exhausted, but if the car didn't move, the scientist would say you had done no work on the car. As you can see, there is a big difference between the everyday use and the scientific use of the word "work."

Two things must happen for a force to do work on an object. First, the force must push or pull on the object. Second, the object must move some distance. Both must happen; otherwise, no work is done. For example, suppose you pick up a heavy book bag and put it on your back. Now a scientist would say that you have done work on the book bag. But exactly how much did you do?

Work is done when a force acts on an object that moves some distance while the force acts.

It's not hard to figure out. Multiply the force needed to lift the bag by the distance the object was lifted. That's it. In other words, for the scientist:

Force (F) × Distance (d) = Work (W)

In mathematical terms, this could be expressed as

Fd = W

The amount of work done equals the product of the force (in newtons) times the distance (in meters) through which the force acts—

Force (N) × Distance (m) = Work (N-m)

When force and distance are measured using newtons and meters, work is measured in units called newton-meters (N-m). A newton-meter is also called a joule (J), for James Joule, who made important discoveries about work and energy. Work and energy are both measured in newton-meters or joules. In this module you will use newton-meters as the unit of measure for work. Using this unit will remind you how to calculate a value for work. Here's an example:

Michael lifts his book bag, which weighs 25 N, from the floor to a desktop that is 0.80 m above the floor. How much work does Michael do on the bag?

Force × Distance = 25 N × 0.80 m = 20.0 N-m = Work

Michael does 20.0 N-m of work on the book bag.

Why can the weight lifter in the photo on the right be said to be doing no work on the barbell? Because the barbell isn't moving; the weight lifter pushes upward, but the barbell stays in one place above his head. The product of force multiplied by the distance moved equals zero. Remember, according to the scientific definition, work is the product of two things—force and distance moved.

A weight lifter does a lot of work to lift a barbell above his head. The work he does is the product of the weight he lifts and the distance he lifts it.

This weight lifter is holding the barbell steady over his head. Is he doing any work on the barbell now? Why or why not?

Inquiry 8.1
Measuring the Work Done Across a Surface

PROCEDURE

1. In this inquiry, you will use the data on friction that you collected during Inquiry 6.1. In that inquiry, you calculated the average force on the spring scale as you pulled a wooden block across different surfaces. Return to Student Sheet 6.1 and find the average force data for each surface.

2. In the first data column of Table 1 on Student Sheet 8.1a, write the figure that represents the average force on the block as it moved across each surface. This is the effort force—the effort you exerted on the block to pull it across each surface.

3. You pulled the wooden block a known distance—0.27 m (27 cm)—each time. Record "0.27 m" as the effort distance for all surfaces.

4. Multiply the effort force by 0.27 m—the effort distance—to find the work done on the block for each surface (remember to use N-m as the work unit).

5. Complete the table on Student Sheet 8.1a and answer the questions.

Inquiry 8.2
Measuring the Work To Lift a Load

PROCEDURE

1. Set up a pegboard assembly as you did in Lesson 7 (see Figure 7.1). Connect three batteries in series to the motor (see Figure 8.1).

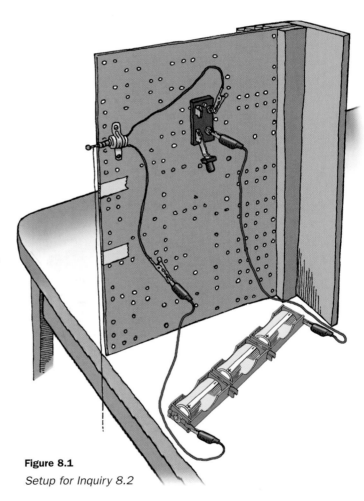

Figure 8.1
Setup for Inquiry 8.2

2. Use the tape to mark a vertical distance of 10 cm on the pegboard, as shown in Figure 8.1.

3. Use what you learned in Lesson 7 to attach the string to the motor so the motor exerts the greatest force on the washers. Attach a paper clip to the string so the bottom of the string is below the 10-cm piece of tape, as shown in Figure 8.1.

4. In Lesson 7, you measured how much force the motor exerts when it is connected to three batteries arranged in series. Record that force on Student Sheet 8.2 at Step 1.

5. Use the force the motor exerts to calculate how much work the motor does when it raises a load 10 cm (0.10 m). Record your calculation on Student Sheet 8.2 at Step 2.

6. Put six washers on the paper clip.

7. Close the switch and run the motor. Does the motor lift the washers? If not, remove a washer and try again. Keep removing washers one at a time until the motor can lift the remaining washers.

8. How much work did the motor have to do to lift the washers 10 cm? To answer that question, use a spring scale to weigh the washers. Record the weight on Student Sheet 8.2 at Step 3. Then multiply the weight by the distance (0.10 m) to get the work done in lifting the washers. Show your work on Student Sheet 8.2 at Step 4.

9. You have calculated work in two ways. One way was using the force of the motor. The other way was using the weight of the washers. How do the two values for work compare? Record your answer in your science notebook.

10. Now build your sled using K'NEX® parts and 14 washers. Follow Figures 8.3 through 8.5 to assemble the sled. The finished sled will look like the one shown in Figure 8.2.

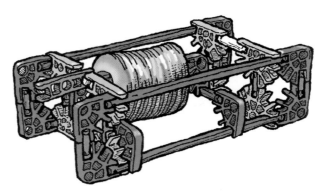

Figure 8.2 *The assembled sled*

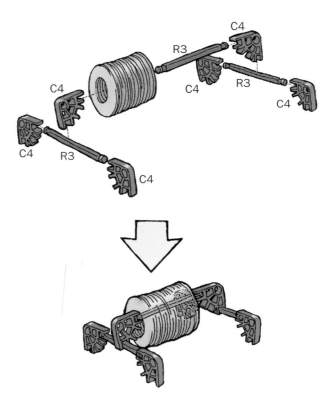

Figure 8.3 *How to assemble the washer seat for K'NEX® sled*

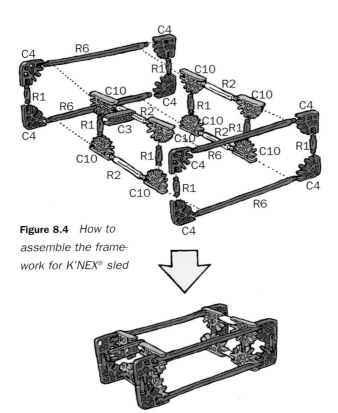

Figure 8.4 *How to assemble the framework for K'NEX® sled*

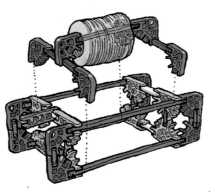

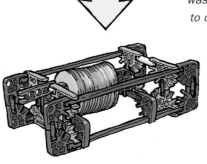

Figure 8.5 *Putting the framework and washer seat together to complete the sled*

11. When you finish assembling the sled, estimate its weight. Describe how you made your estimate. Record your estimate on Student Sheet 8.2 at Step 5, and describe how you made your estimate in your science notebook.

12. Now actually measure and record the weight of the sled using a spring scale. Record this on Student Sheet 8.2 at Step 6.

13. How accurate was your estimate of the weight? Record your answer in your science notebook.

14. Calculate the work it will take to lift the sled 10 cm. Show your work on Student Sheet 8.2 at Step 7.

15. Try lifting the sled with the motor. Record what happens in your science notebook.

REFLECTING ON WHAT YOU'VE DONE

Discuss the following questions with your lab partner, and share your results and observations during a class discussion.

A. Look at your table on Student Sheet 8.1a. Why do you think different amounts of work were done as you pulled the block across different surfaces?

B. In Inquiry 8.2, when you tried to lift the sled with the motor, what happened?

C. How much work did the motor do on the sled?

D. Compare the maximum force of the motor with the weight of the sled. Explain why the motor could not do the work it takes to lift the sled.

E. Since the motor cannot exert a greater force, think of ways to get the motor to do the work to lift the sled. List your ideas.

MEASURING UP

You can't get very far in science if you don't know how to measure and count accurately. And accurate measurements aren't worth anything if they can't be expressed in a way that anyone—even someone working on a similar problem around the world—can understand. In other words, scientists need standardized units of measure. Here is some information about the units of measure in the metric system, which you are using in this module.

The metric system is part of the International System of Units, a measuring system used throughout most of the world. The names of metric units identify what they measure. Meters (m), milliliters (mL), and kilograms (kg) are examples of metric units.

Some metric units are named after a scientist who made important contributions to a particular field. For example, Sir Isaac Newton explained how forces act on objects and the unit of force in the metric system is the newton (N). James Joule explained the relationship between work and energy, and the unit of energy and work is—you guessed it—the joule (J). André Ampère gave his name to the "ampere," the unit of electrical current ("amps," for short). Italian scientist Alessandro Volta gets credit for the volt, which is used to express the electric potential of a battery. The unit of power is the watt (W), named after the Scottish engineer James Watt. □

QUESTIONS

1. Why are units of measure needed?
2. There are other metric units named for scientists. Look up the metric system and find a unit named for a scientist. What was the scientist's complete name? What did he or she study?

KLAMATH FALLS—
A Real Hot Spot

Klamath Falls, Oregon, gets its share of snow every winter. But not all the residents of this city of 18,000 have to worry about shoveling their sidewalks or getting out the snowplows to clear the roads. Geothermal energy, pumped through a system of hot water pipes flowing underground, melts the snow and ice on some sidewalks and roads.

Geothermal energy is heat energy that comes from inside the earth. The deeper into the earth one goes, the warmer it becomes. Scientists think that the temperature at the very core of the earth may be as high as 5000 °C (9000 °F). In areas of geothermal activity such as Klamath Falls, water that has been heated deep under ground comes close enough to the earth's surface to be put to work. Sometimes the water even bubbles up above the surface of the earth and forms hot springs.

The people in Klamath Falls are not the first to use geothermal energy. It has been used in North America for more than 10,000 years. Archaeologists have found evidence that early Native Americans used hot springs to keep warm. They also used the water for cleaning and cooking. Early European settlers in the western United States built spas and resorts around natural hot springs. Some people believe that these waters have healing powers. Everyone who visits these spas finds that the warm water, which has a high mineral content, provides an invigorating natural bath.

In Klamath Falls, geothermal energy is put to practical uses as well. In addition to reducing the need for snowplows, it helps heat public buildings. Geothermal water is piped into a heat exchanger, which transfers the heat energy from the hot

PHOTO COURTESY HERALD AND NEWS, KLAMATH FALLS, OREGON

A worker lays down pipes that will carry hot water beneath the streets and sidewalks of Klamath Falls to keep them free of ice and snow in the winter.

groundwater to clean water in a pipe network. The heated water circulates through the pipes and heats buildings around the city.

Some businesses in the city use geothermal energy in creative ways. Geothermal water is piped through greenhouses to keep them warm in winter. The fish-growing industry uses the water to heat tanks. Fish raised in these tanks grow faster than do those raised in colder tanks. Other businesses use heat from geothermal sources to dry vegetables and lumber.

In the United States, some western states have geothermal power plants that use steam pressure that has come from beneath the earth to turn a turbine that operates an electrical generator. Geothermal power plants produce electricity in many other countries, including Iceland, New Zealand, Italy, Argentina, Japan, and Kenya.

Even though geothermal energy has been used

In Iceland, a woman bakes bread using a geothermal oven.

for thousands of years, its potential is still mostly untapped. As people become more concerned about controlling pollution and making the best use of natural resources, geothermal energy is bound to become more widely used. □

Bathers in Iceland enjoy the warm waters outside a geothermal power plant. The water stays warm throughout the winter.

Power of a Motor

The motor in a small tugboat has enough power to pull a much bigger ship along slowly.

© RICHARD DURING/ALLSTOCK/PNI

INTRODUCTION

How powerful is the motor you have been using in your investigations? In previous lessons, you examined its ability to lift loads under different operating conditions. You also measured the work performed as the motor lifted a load of washers, and you found that the motor could not lift a sled. In Lesson 9, you will learn how to calculate the motor's power output by measuring the time it takes the motor to do a specific amount of work. You will also discover how the motor's power depends on the number of batteries connected to it.

OBJECTIVES FOR THIS LESSON

Calculate the power of a motor.

Investigate how the time it takes a motor to lift a load depends on the number of batteries connected in series to the motor.

Investigate how a motor's power depends on the number of batteries connected in series to the motor.

Getting Started

1. If you have not already done so, read "Work, Energy, and Power" on page 84. Then answer the following questions in your science notebook:

   A. *How are work and energy related?*

   B. *How do you calculate power?*

   C. *What are the most commonly used units of measure for power?*

2. Before you start this inquiry, you need to practice calculating power. Two situations are described here. For each, calculate the power output. Practice these calculations on your own, writing them in your science notebook. You may want to use them later to help with calculations for this lab.

   A. *A girl pushes at a steady pace with a force of 8.0 N on a box. She moves the box 3.0 m in 5.0 s. What is her power output?*

   B. *A motor steadily lifts a load that weighs 5.0 N a distance of 1.5 m in 2.0 s. What is the power output of the motor?*

3. What factors might affect the time it takes a motor to lift a load? Discuss your ideas with the class.

MATERIALS FOR LESSON 9

For you and your lab partner

- 1 pegboard assembly
- 3 large washers
- 1 electric motor with wire leads and alligator clips
- 1 motor pulley with nail
- 1 motor clamp
- 3 machine screws and wing nuts
- 3 D-cell batteries
- 3 D-cell battery holders
- 1 knife switch
- 5 insulated connector wires with alligator clips
- 1 large paper clip
- 1 piece of string
- 1 meterstick
- 1 0- to 2.5-N spring scale
- 1 piece of masking tape
- 1 student timer

WORK, ENERGY, AND POWER

You learned in Lesson 8 that work is done when a force acts on an object as the object moves over a distance. When work is done, energy changes from one form to another. Energy is defined as the ability to do work.

In Lesson 8, when you connected the battery to the motor, the battery's chemical energy converted to electrical energy and then to mechanical energy in the motor. The motor's shaft turned and pulled a load of washers. As the motor lifted the load, the motor's mechanical energy changed to other forms of energy. Some of the mechanical energy of the motor became kinetic energy in the moving load and heat in the motor, while some of it became gravitational energy in the load as the load was lifted.

In this lesson, you will explore the time it takes the motor to lift a load. How long a motor takes to lift a load reveals something about the motor's power. To find the motor's power, you need to know how much work the motor does each second.

Power is the rate of doing work, or the amount of work done each second.

$$\text{Power} = \frac{\text{Work}}{\text{Time}}$$

The common unit of power is the watt (W), named for Scottish engineer James Watt, who improved steam engines in the late 18th century by making them safer and more efficient. One watt is equal to doing 1 newton-meter (or joule) of work in 1 second.

$$1 \text{ watt} = \frac{1 \text{ newton-meter}}{1 \text{ second}}$$

To calculate power in watts, measure work in newton-meters (N-m) and time in seconds (s), and then divide the work by the time it takes to do the work:

$$\text{Power (W)} = \frac{\text{Work (N-m)}}{\text{Time (s)}}$$

Because work changes energy, power can also be defined as a measure of the rate at which energy is supplied or used. A 60-W lightbulb uses 60 N-m (joules) of energy each second it operates. A 100-W motor can do 100 N-m (joules) of work each second.

People use other units to measure power. In situations where the watt is too small a unit, people measure power in larger units, called kilowatts (kW). One kW equals 1000 W. Both words describe both electrical power and mechanical power, like the power of your motor.

You may have heard of another unit of power—horsepower. Horsepower is often used to describe the power of car engines and motors. You will read about horsepower later in this lesson, in a reader called "How Many Horses?"

Inquiry 9.1
Measuring Power

PROCEDURE

1. Set up the pegboard assembly as shown in Figure 9.1. Include each of the following steps:

A. Make sure the string is long enough to reach from the motor to the floor.

B. Tie one end of the string to the nail on the motor shaft. Put a small piece of tape over the string where it is tied to the nail to keep the string from slipping when lifting the load.

C. Attach three washers to a paper clip at the free end of the string, so that the hanging washers just touch the floor.

2. You will measure and record the time it takes the motor to lift three washers when one battery is connected, and then when two batteries and three batteries are connected in series. Before you begin, design a data table in your science notebook with columns for three time measurements and an average time for each of the three battery arrangements.

3. Connect one battery to the motor. Close the switch. Record how many seconds it takes the motor to lift three washers to the tabletop. Lower the washers until they just touch the floor. Raise the washers again and record the time. Repeat this for a total of three measurements.

4. Record the three time measurements in your data table. Calculate and record the average time of the three trials.

5. Discuss the following questions with your partner and record the answers in your notebook:

A. What effect would adding a second battery in series have on the time it takes the motor to lift the washers?

B. Why do you think this will happen?

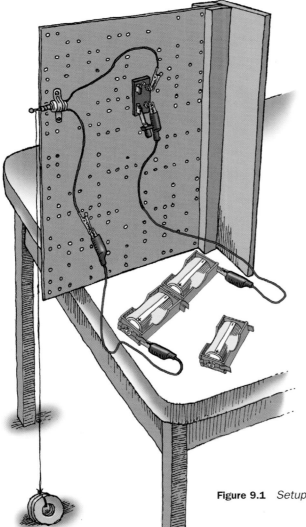

Figure 9.1 *Setup for Inquiry 9.1*

6. Now try it. Measure and record the time it takes to lift the washers to the tabletop. As before, record the time measurements in your data table and then calculate and record the average time. How well did you predict what would happen? Record your comments in your notebook.

7. Add a third battery in series to the motor. Determine the average time it takes to lift the washers in the same way.

8. Using the information recorded in your data table, graph the average time it takes to lift the washers versus the number of batteries in series.

9. Use the spring scale to measure the weight (in newtons) of the three washers. Record this information in your science notebook.

10. Measure the vertical distance (in meters) that the motor lifted the washers each time.

11. Using the weight and distance measurements, calculate and record in your science notebook how much work the motor did to lift the washers.

12. Calculate and record how much power the motor provided using one battery. Remember:

$$\text{Power (W)} = \frac{\text{Work (N-m)}}{\text{Time (s)}}$$

13. How much power did the motor provide using two batteries? Three batteries? In your science notebook, make a table with columns for "Power" and "Number of batteries." Record the power data in the table.

14. Use your table to plot a graph that represents "Power" versus "Number of batteries."

REFLECTING ON WHAT YOU'VE DONE

Answer the following questions. Support your answers with evidence from your data. Be prepared to discuss your answers with the class.

A. Did the amount of work done each time by the motor to lift the load depend on the number of batteries used in the circuit? Why or why not?

B. Suppose you made a graph of the work it takes to lift the washers versus the number of batteries. Describe what that graph would look like or draw a picture of such a graph.

C. What changed as you added more batteries?

D. Look at your graph of "Average time to lift" versus "Number of batteries." Is the time needed to lift the washers related to the number of batteries added in series? How?

E. Look at your graph of "Power" versus "Number of batteries." Does the power to lift the washers depend on the number of batteries in series? How?

F. Suppose you need to lift a larger load. What can you do to make the motor produce more power?

G. The batteries supplied energy for the motor circuit. Did the motor use all the energy supplied by the battery to lift the load? If not, what other forms does the battery's energy become?

HOW MANY HORSES?

It was the late 1800s, and engineer James Watt was stumped. He'd just figured out a way to make steam engines operate much more efficiently. He wanted to start manufacturing and selling his new invention. But how could he describe how powerful these amazing engines were?

Watt's answer? Compare the power of the steam engine with something that people were very familiar with: the power of a horse.

In Watt's day, ponies were used to pull ropes attached to platforms that lifted coal to the surface of the earth. Watt measured how much these loads weighed. Then he determined how far the ponies could raise them in one minute. Using these measurements, he calculated how much work a pony could do in a minute.

At that time, the unit of work used by British scientists was the foot-pound (ft-lb). On the basis of his observations and calculations, Watt found that a pony could do 22,000 ft-lb of work a minute. Because he figured that the average horse was as powerful as 1.5 ponies, he multiplied the power of one pony (22,000 ft-lb of work per minute) by 1.5 and called it 1 horsepower (hp).

Ponies sometimes provided the power to pull loaded carts from mines.

The power of horses is still used to do important work.

In other words, 1 hp is 33,000 ft-lb of work per minute, or 550 ft-lb of work per second. This means that an average horse can lift a 550-lb load a distance of 1 foot in 1 second.

Horsepower can be translated into watts (W): 1 hp equals 750 W. A 350-hp engine, therefore, has the same power as a 262,500-W engine. But when numbers get as big as this, you can see that watts aren't a convenient way of expressing the power of engines. Using the word "horsepower" also probably makes drivers feel closer to the good old days—when people were pioneers and mustangs were horses! ☐

Horsepower is still used to describe the power of motors. How much horsepower does this outboard motor provide?

QUESTIONS

1. Why do you think James Watt used a horse as a measure of a unit of power?
2. How did Watt decide the value of 1 horsepower?
3. Why is the horsepower still a useful unit of power?

The Power of Nature

Earthquake damage

Tidal waves wallop buildings. Earthquakes flatten highway overpasses. Tornadoes fling cars and trucks from one place to another. The power of nature is a hot topic on disaster shows and the evening news. But do you ever really think about how much energy is released in these disasters?

When a tornado's winds reach 320 kilometers per hour, that tornado is releasing energy at a rate of 1 trillion joules per second. Tornadoes sprout from the dark clouds of thunderstorms, which are even more powerful

Powerful tornadoes can strike suddenly and cause great damage.

than the tornadoes they spawn. Thunderstorms large enough to generate tornadoes can release 40 trillion joules of energy per second. (That's 40, plus 12 zeroes.) Lightning is another product of thunderstorms. A single bolt of lightning produces power at the same rate that a tornado does, but the energy is in a different form and is released in a shorter period of time than a tornado's energy.

How do all these billions and trillions relate to daily life? The energy generated by one bolt of lightning could light a 100-watt bulb for three months. When a ton of dynamite explodes, it produces about 63 million joules of energy. A tornado releases more than 15,000 times that much energy every second. Hurricanes, too. The energy a hurricane releases in 24 hours is equal to all the electricity used in the United States over a period of six months.

Nature doesn't limit its displays of power to storms. Volcanoes can launch huge boulders 10 kilometers through the air. Earthquakes can produce as much power as a small nuclear weapon can. Earthquakes on the seafloor cause giant waves called tsunamis (a Japanese word). Tsunamis can cross oceans and become as high as a 10-story building by the time they reach land. Tsunamis this powerful can demolish entire coastal cities.

The most memorable displays of nature's power are destructive, but the power of nature isn't always violent. The

© JOHNNY AUTERY

A powerful bolt of lightning releases a tremendous amount of energy in a very short time.

power of oceans and rivers—hydroelectric power—produces up to 13 percent of the energy consumed in the United States. Central and South America get as much as 27 percent of their energy from the power of moving water. And each day, more solar energy reaches the earth than the planet's population could use in 25 years.

So next time you hear the rumble of thunder, feel the heat of the sun on your face, or watch ocean waves crash onto the beach, take a moment to consider the power of nature. ☐

Volcanic eruptions are powerful enough to send ash and dust many kilometers into the atmosphere.

The power of nature can be harnessed. At Glen Canyon Dam, the power of falling water is used to generate electrical energy.

10

Assessing What You Know

Students setting up equipment for the performance assessment

INTRODUCTION

In the previous nine lessons, you investigated energy, forces, work, and power. You explored how energy is transformed—how it changes from one form to another—and you examined the nature of different forces. You learned how to calculate work and power, and you investigated how the power of a motor depends on the number of batteries used. You also learned how to graph data and draw conclusions from your observations.

This lesson gives you a chance to show how well you learned the skills and concepts presented in Lessons 1 through 9. You will complete an activity in which you set up and use equipment to collect data. You will then draw conclusions based on your data. Next, you will graph and analyze data and interpret its meaning. Finally, you will complete short-response and multiple-choice questions.

OBJECTIVES FOR THIS LESSON

Manipulate equipment.

Gather and record data.

Interpret data and draw conclusions based on the data.

Demonstrate knowledge of energy, forces, work, and power.

Relate your knowledge to new situations.

Getting Started

1. Review the objectives of this assessment with the class.

2. Listen as your teacher describes the assessment and its parts.

3. Make sure you have sharpened pencils and other materials your teacher says you need.

MATERIALS FOR LESSON 10

For you

- 1 copy of Inquiry Master 10.5: Multiple-Choice Questions
- 1 copy of Student Sheet 10.1: Performance Assessment
- 1 copy of Student Sheet 10.2: Data Analysis
- 1 copy of Student Sheet 10.3: Multiple-Choice and Short-Answer Response Sheet

For your group

- 1 copy of Inquiry Master 10.1: Performance Assessment Directions
- 1 pegboard assembly
- 7 large washers
- 1 electric motor with wire leads and alligator clips
- 1 motor pulley with nail
- 1 motor clamp
- 3 machine screws with wing nuts
- 1 miniature lightbulb
- 1 miniature lightbulb holder
- 1 black insulated connector wire with alligator clips
- 1 red insulated connector wire with alligator clips
- 1 large paper clip
- 1 piece of string
- 1 meterstick
- 1 0- to 2.5-N spring scale

Period 1
Performance Assessment

PROCEDURE

1. Read Inquiry Master 10.1: Performance Assessment Directions. Ask your teacher to explain anything that is not clear.

2. Go to your station with your lab partner when your teacher asks you to.

3. Complete the activity as described on the inquiry master and record your responses on Student Sheet 10.1. Be sure to complete all activities and answer all questions.

4. When you finish the performance assessment, your teacher will collect your students sheets and give you further directions.

Period 2

Data Analysis and Multiple-Choice and Short-Response Questions

PROCEDURE

1. Do this part of the assessment on your own. Follow the directions on Student Sheet 10.2: Data Analysis. Your teacher will collect the student sheet when you have completed the data analysis.

2. Read the multiple-choice questions on Inquiry Master 10.5: Multiple-Choice and Short-Answer Questions. Then, on Student Sheet 10.3: Multiple-Choice and Short-Answer Response Sheet, circle the choice that best answers each question or completes each statement.

3. When you have completed the multiple-choice questions, answer the short-answer questions on Student Sheet 10.3. Use complete sentences. Your teacher will tell you what to do with the student sheet when you have completed it.

REFLECTING ON WHAT YOU'VE DONE

1. Discuss with the class the results of the performance assessment. Evaluate how well you followed directions and used the equipment. Were your conclusions based on your observations and data?

2. Your teacher will show you a graph of the data you used in the data-analysis assessment. Think about the following questions:

    A. *How well did you follow good graphing procedures?*

    B. *Were your conclusions based on evidence from the graph?*

3. Ask questions and clarify your understanding of any of the multiple-choice questions or short-answer responses if you answered any incorrectly.

CARS: ENERGY TO BURN

Cars racing at the Miami Indy Car Race in Florida

During the first nine lessons of this module, you've learned about energy transformation, force, work, and power. How can you tie these ideas together into a single application? Take a ride in an automobile!

All cars, no matter how big or small, do two basic things. First, they transform chemical energy to heat energy and energy of motion. Second, they convert energy of motion to heat energy.

The heart of a car is its engine. In the engine, a fuel (usually gasoline) burns in a cylinder, which is a closed container about the size of a 1-liter milk carton. As the fuel burns, it creates hot gases. These gases expand and press against the piston, which is a movable block at one end of the cylinder. Through a combination of rods, shafts, and gears, the piston is connected to the wheels of the car. The pressure of the expanding gases makes the piston move. This causes the wheels to rotate and makes the car move.

The moving car has kinetic energy, which is energy of motion. At this point, an important energy conversion has taken place: Some of the energy stored in the fuel has become energy of motion.

But there's something else to think about. Not all the energy released when gasoline burns goes to help move the car. Most of it becomes heat energy. That is why the car needs a radiator. The radiator is the center of the car's cooling system. The cooling system circulates water and a coolant around the engine to prevent it from overheating.

Once a car is moving, the next important energy transformation comes when it's time to stop. Friction helps here. Friction from the brakes stops the car; in other words, it reduces the car's kinetic energy. When the brake pads rub against the brake drums, the brakes get very hot—a sign that energy of movement is being transformed to heat energy. By the time that a car stops, most of the chemical energy that had been stored in the fuel tank has been converted to heat.

© BOB DAEMMRICH/STOCK, BOSTON/PNI

Looking under the hood. The heart of a car is its engine.

In a moving car, energy conversions are taking place continually. That's why it takes a constant supply of fuel to keep it going. When the fuel is used up, drivers need more. That means a stop at the fuel pump. Once the tank is filled, you have energy to burn! ☐

Fill 'er up!

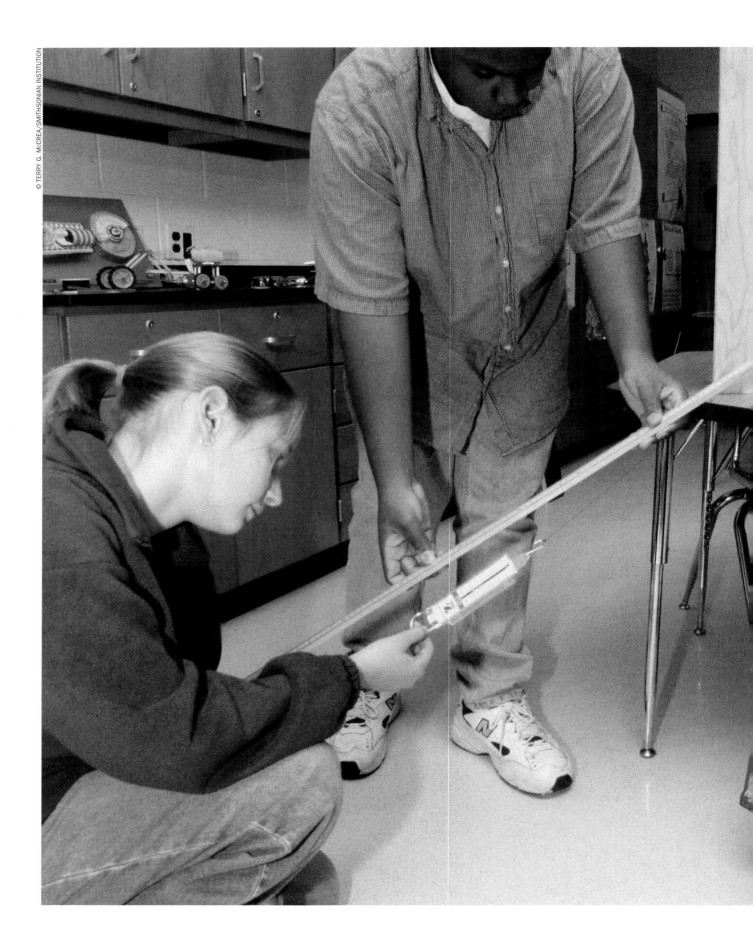

PART 2 Machines

11

The Inclined Plane

Inclined planes make getting around easier.

INTRODUCTION

Have you ever used a machine to do a job? What kind of machine was it? What did it do for you? What exactly do machines do?

In the next three lessons, you will explore these questions by investigating how three simple machines—inclined planes, pulleys, and levers—operate. Understanding simple machines will help you understand more complex machines, such as bulldozers, cranes, and bicycles. Later in this module, you will have the opportunity to use a machine and a motor together.

You will begin your investigation of machines by focusing on the inclined plane. Inclined planes are ramps. You see them everywhere. Many places have ramps to help physically disabled people enter and exit buildings. Sometimes people use ramps to move heavy loads. If you had to raise a heavy load to some height, would you rather lift it straight up or push it along an incline? Think about that as you do this inquiry.

OBJECTIVES FOR THIS LESSON

Learn how an inclined plane works.

Investigate how the force to pull a load up an incline depends on the slope of the incline.

Compare the work done in pulling a load up an incline with the work done in lifting the load straight up.

Getting Started

1. Review what you wrote in your science notebook about frictional force in Lesson 6. Then discuss this with your lab partner and the class.

2. Discuss the following questions with the class:

   A. *Have you ever seen a ramp used to move an object or a person onto a platform or to a higher position? If so, where?*

   B. *Did the ramp have a gentle slope or a steep slope?*

   C. *Why do you think a ramp was used?*

3. Have your science notebook ready so you can record your data and answers to questions in Inquiries 11.1 and 11.2.

MATERIALS FOR LESSON 11

For you

1 copy of Student Sheet 11.1: Forces on a Cart on the Inclined Plane

1 copy of Student Sheet 11.2: What Is the Work Done Using an Inclined Plane?

For your group

1 inclined plane (wooden board)
1 pegboard double loop hook
1 K'NEX® sled (from Lesson 8)
1 pegboard assembly
1 large paper clip
1 0- to 2.5-N spring scale
1 0- to 10-N spring scale
1 meterstick

2 pieces of masking tape
Additional K'NEX® parts for wheel assembly (see Appendix A: Directory of K'NEX® Parts):
   4 gray connectors (C1)
   2 red rods (R6)
   4 small wheels (W1)

Inquiry 11.1
Measuring Forces on a Cart on an Inclined Plane

PROCEDURE

1. For this inquiry, you will use the sled you built in Lesson 8. Attach a spring scale to the sled's orange connector and measure the force required to pull the sled at a steady speed across a table. Record this force in your science notebook.

2. Why does it take this force to move the sled?

3. Now add wheels to your sled to turn it into a "cart," as shown in Figure 11.1.

4. Use the spring scale to measure the force needed to pull the cart at a slow, steady speed across the tabletop. Record the force in your science notebook.

5. The force you exert to pull the sled or cart is called the effort force. How does the effort force needed to pull the cart compare with the effort force needed to pull the sled? Why was there a difference between the two forces?

6. Using the double loop hook, attach the inclined plane to the pegboard, as shown in Figure 11.2. Now place the cart on the inclined plane. Measure and record the force required to hold the cart on the plane. What creates the force on the cart on the inclined plane?

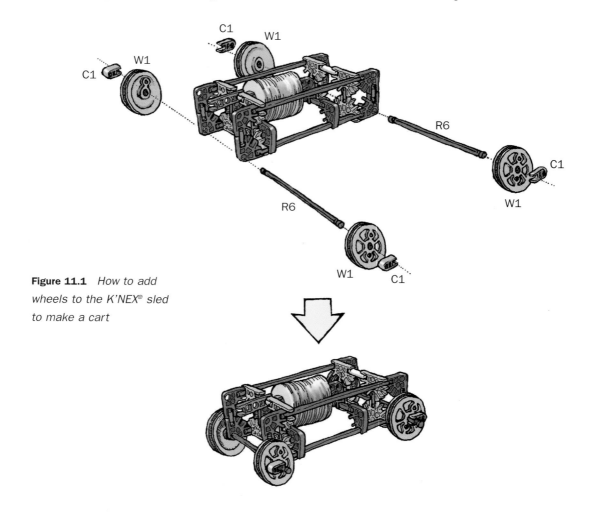

Figure 11.1 *How to add wheels to the K'NEX® sled to make a cart*

7. Suppose you pulled the cart up an inclined plane like the one shown in Figure 11.2. How do you think the effort force needed to pull the cart up the incline at a slow, steady speed would compare with the effort force needed to move the sled across the table? Explain your reasoning.

8. Test your prediction and record the results.

9. What do you predict will happen to the effort force required to move the cart up the inclined plane if the slope of the incline is increased? Develop your prediction with your lab partners and record your prediction on Student Sheet 11.1: Forces on a Cart on the Inclined Plane.

10. Design a procedure to test your prediction. Use equipment in the materials list for this inquiry. Describe your procedure in the space provided on your student sheet. Make sure your procedure describes the way you will measure the slope of the incline.

11. Draw a data table on the student sheet to record your measurements.

12. Carry out your procedure and test your prediction.

13. Examine your results and decide with your partner how you will analyze your data. Explain or show your analysis of your data on your student sheet.

14. On your student sheet, write a conclusion supported by your data about effort force to move the cart along the incline and the slope of the incline.

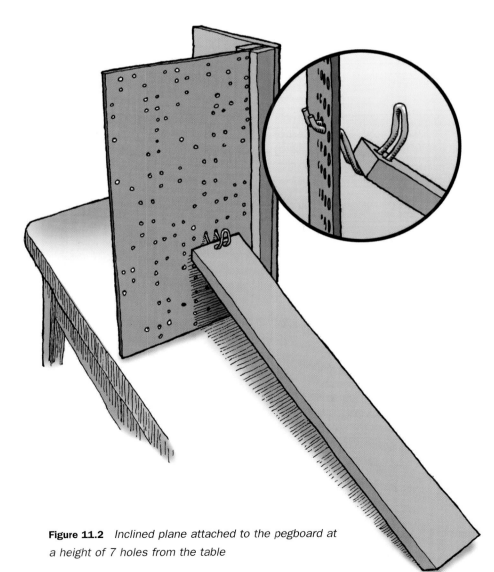

Figure 11.2 *Inclined plane attached to the pegboard at a height of 7 holes from the table*

Inquiry 11.2
Measuring Work on a Cart on an Inclined Plane

PROCEDURE

1. Record your data, calculations, and answers for this inquiry on Student Sheet 11.2: What Is the Work Done Using an Inclined Plane?

2. In this inquiry, you are asked to lift a cart, or load, a vertical distance of 0.10 meter (m) each time. This vertical distance to which you lift the cart is called the *load distance.* The force you need to exert to lift the cart straight up is called the *load force.* Figure 11.3 shows how to measure load force and load distance.

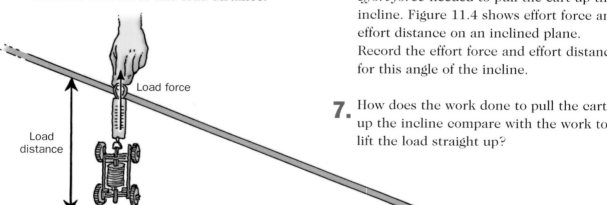

Figure 11.3 *How to measure load force and load distance*

3. Use the spring scale to measure the force to lift the cart straight up through a distance of 0.10 m. Use the load force and load distance to calculate the amount of work to lift the cart.

4. Instead of moving the cart straight up, suppose you pulled the cart up the incline so it moved 0.10 m vertically. Would the work you did pulling it up the incline be more, less, or the same as the work needed to lift

the cart 0.10 m straight up? Record your prediction and explain your reasoning.

5. Set up the pegboard and inclined plane so the inclined plane is attached at hole 7, counting from the bottom of the pegboard. Place the cart on the inclined plane and hold it so it does not roll down the incline. Discuss with your group how you can tell when the cart has moved the load distance (0.10 m straight up) when you pull the cart up the incline. Share your ideas with the class.

6. Now pull the cart up the incline so that it moves a load distance of 0.10 m. Measure the distance the cart moves along the incline. This distance is the *effort distance.* The spring scale measures the *effort force* needed to pull the cart up the incline. Figure 11.4 shows effort force and effort distance on an inclined plane. Record the effort force and effort distance for this angle of the incline.

7. How does the work done to pull the cart up the incline compare with the work to lift the load straight up?

8. Repeat these measurements of effort force and effort distance with different slopes of the incline. Set the inclined plane at four different slopes, and each time record the effort force and effort distance to raise the cart 0.10 m along the incline. Figure 11.5 shows different inclines positioned so the load distance is constant at 0.10 m while the angle of incline changes. For each slope, measure the effort distance and the effort force while raising the cart the load distance (0.10 m) each time.

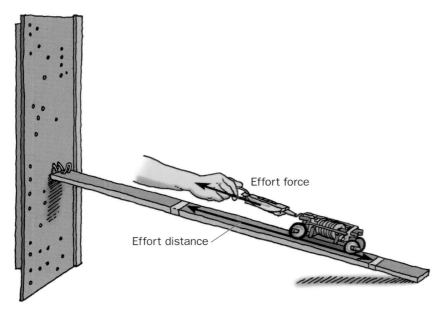

Figure 11.4 *Effort force and effort distance on an inclined plane*

9. Complete Table 1 on Student Sheet 11.2 by calculating the work you did each time you applied the effort force along the plane. Remember: Use newtons (N) to measure force and meters (m) to measure distance. Calculate work in newton-meters (N-m) or joules (J). If a force of 1 N moves an object 1 m, then 1 N-m or 1 J of work is done. Be sure to use the correct units in your data table.

10. How does the work needed to pull the cart up the inclined plane compare with the work needed to lift the cart straight up? With the rest of the class, develop an explanation of your results. Record your answers in your science notebook.

REFLECTING ON WHAT YOU'VE DONE
Answer the following questions in your science notebook.

A. On the basis of the results of these inquiries, how would you define a machine?

B. In your view, is an inclined plane a machine?

C. Why are ramps for people with physical disabilities long and gently sloping, rather than short and steep?

D. Suppose you repeated Inquiry 11.2 with a sled instead of a cart. Would you get different results? If so, how would they be different?

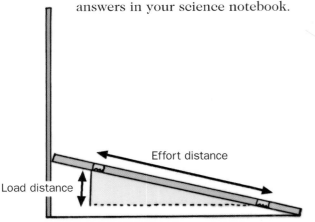

Figure 11.5 *For the same load distance, the effort distance changes when the slope of the incline changes. What happens to the effort force when the slope of the inclined plane changes?*

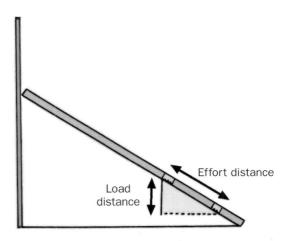

Escape Route in Johnstown

A century or so ago, the little city of Johnstown, Pennsylvania, was a disaster waiting to happen. Like many other American cities, Johnstown had been established in a river valley. The Little Conemaugh River, which ran through the city, had always been prone to flooding. As the city grew, the banks of the river were narrowed to make room for more buildings. The possibility of flooding increased. The South Fork Dam, which held back the river and formed a lake about 22 kilometers upstream, was poorly maintained.

May 1889 was a rainy month in Johnstown. At 4:00 P.M. on May 31, the dam broke and released 20 million tons of water into the narrow valley.

The resulting flood and fires killed more than 2200 people.

Finding a Solution

The people of Johnstown knew that a disaster like the flood of 1889 could happen again. They needed a plan. They decided that the solution would be to have a way to get people out of the city quickly in the case of another flood. An inclined plane would do the trick, they reasoned.

They hired the Cambria Iron Company to build the inclined plane. Two years later, the work was completed. The inclined plane, measuring nearly 300 meters in length, was designed

Flood damage in Johnstown, Pennsylvania, in 1889

as a modified railroad. To match the steepness of the valley, the inclined plane was built at a grade of 71 percent. This earned it a spot in *The Guinness Book of World Records* as the steepest vehicular inclined plane in the world.

Riding in a railroad car that goes up at a sharp angle would be uncomfortable. To make the ride easier, the cars for the inclined plane were specially designed to stay level as they descend into and climb out of the valley. Each car can hold up to 15 tons of cargo, including people, bikes, cars, and—originally— horses and wagons.

Today the Johnstown inclined plane is mainly a tourist attraction. But during floods in 1936 and 1997, it was used successfully to evacuate valley residents and to carry rescue personnel, equipment, and supplies into the valley. ☐

The Johnstown Vehicular Incline

QUESTIONS

1. In what parts of the world besides Johnstown, Pennsylvania, do you think you might find vehicular inclines?

2. Visit the Internet and see if you can find an example of another vehicular incline. Where is it? How steep is it? How long?

The Pulley

Pulleys come in handy when hoisting a sail.

CORBIS/JAMES P. BLAIR

INTRODUCTION

In Lesson 11, you measured forces and distances and you calculated work on an inclined plane. You used the inclined plane to make it easier to raise a load to a certain height. But inclined planes do not work in all situations. For example, suppose you needed to lift a load to a great height but you didn't have space for a long ramp. You would need another kind of machine to do the job. In this lesson, you will use a different machine to lift the sled. That machine is a pulley system.

OBJECTIVES FOR THIS LESSON

Understand how pulleys work.

Construct different pulley systems and use them to lift a load.

Investigate the relationship between effort force and effort distance in pulley systems.

Communicate your observations about pulley systems to your classmates.

Getting Started

1. Describe a situation in which you would need to raise a load to a particular height but for which an inclined plane would not be practical. Discuss your answer with your partners and then share your example with the class.

2. Study the photos in "Uses of Pulleys," on pages 110–111. Then answer the following questions in your science notebook:

A. What is a pulley?

B. How do pulleys help lift loads?

C. What determines how heavy a load a pulley can lift?

MATERIALS FOR LESSON 12

For you

1 copy of Student Sheet 12.1: How Is a Pulley System Used To Do Work?

For your group

1 K'NEX® sled (from Lesson 11)
1 pegboard assembly
4 pegboard hooks
2 large paper clips
1 0- to 2.5-N spring scale
1 0- to 10-N spring scale
1 piece of string
2 metersticks
K'NEX® parts for movable pulley and fixed pulley assemblies (see Appendix A: Directory of K'NEX® Parts):
    6 gray connectors (C1)
    4 red connectors (C4)

6 purple connectors (C6)
6 blue connectors (C7)
2 yellow connectors (C10)
4 white rods (R2)
6 blue rods (R3)
4 red rods (R6)
2 gray rods (R7)
4 large wheels (W2)

USES OF PULLEYS

Pulleys are often used to lift things up very high.

A pulley is a chain or rope wrapped around a wheel. A pulley can change both the amount of effort force needed to do a job and the direction in which the effort force is applied.

CORBIS/THE MARINERS' MUSEUM

The number and strength of supporting ropes in a pulley system determine how large a load the system can lift.

CORBIS/DEAN CONGER

Pulleys like the one on this crane make it possible to build skyscrapers.

CORBIS/JOEL W. ROGERS

Shipyards use cranes and pulleys to load and unload cargo.

Inquiry 12.1
Using Pulleys To Do Work

PROCEDURE

1. In this lesson, you will make a variety of pulley assemblies using K'NEX® parts. First, you need to construct the two pulley assemblies shown in Figures 12.1 and 12.2. Your teacher has a model of each assembly for you to study.

FIXED PULLEY, FRONT VIEW

Figure 12.1 *Fixed pulley assembly*

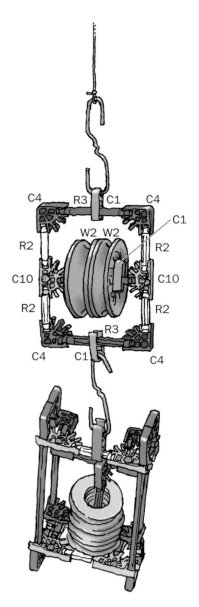

Figure 12.2 *Movable pulley assembly with the sled attached*

2. Attach the sled to the movable pulley assembly. Weigh the movable-pulley-and-sled combination (see Figure 12.3). To lift the pulley assembly, what load force must you exert? Record the load force in Table 1 on Student Sheet 12.1: How Is a Pulley System Used To Do Work?

3. Discuss with your partner why it is necessary to include the weight of the movable pulley in your measurement of load force.

4. Set up a single fixed pulley with the fixed pulley assembly attached to the pegboard, as shown in Figure 12.4. Use enough string so the movable-pulley-and-sled combination rests on the floor when the string is over the pulley.

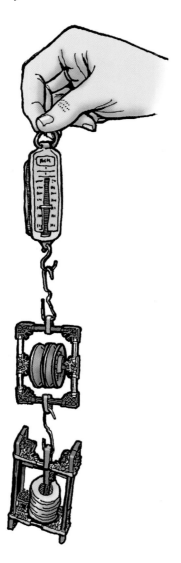

Figure 12.3 *Weighing the movable pulley assembly and sled*

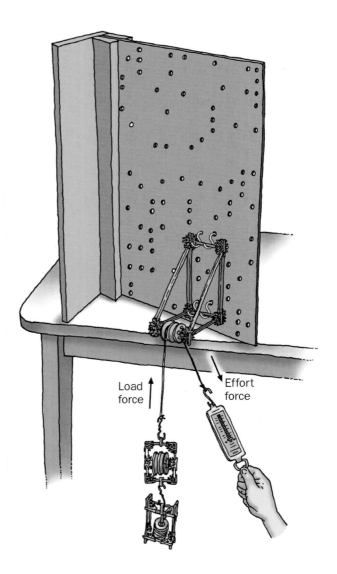

Figure 12.4 *Raising the movable-pulley-and-sled combination using a single fixed pulley*

5. Raise the movable-pulley-and-sled combination at a steady speed to a height of 0.10 m (10 cm) above the floor (see Figure 12.4). Work as a team to measure and record the following on your student sheet:

- how high the load rises (Record this as "Load Distance.")
- how much force the spring scale registers as a team member lifts the load (This is "Effort Force.")
- how far a team member's hand moves as the load rises 0.10 m (This is "Effort Distance.")

6. Answer the following questions in your science notebook:

A. *How did the force you exerted compare with the weight of the movable-pulley-and-sled combination?*

B. *In what direction did the team member pull the string to raise the sled?*

7. Set up the remaining three pulley systems one at a time as shown in Figures 12.5, 12.6, and 12.7. For each setup, measure the effort force and the effort distance needed to raise the movable-pulley-and-sled combination 0.10 m. Add these data to Table 1 on Student Sheet 12.1.

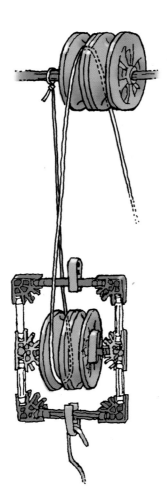

Figure 12.5 *Single fixed, single movable pulley setup*

Figure 12.6 *Double fixed, single movable pulley setup*

Figure 12.7 *Double fixed, double movable pulley setup*

8. Calculate the input work for each pulley arrangement in Table 1 on the student sheet. Input work is the work you did to lift the load. To compute this, multiply effort force by effort distance. Show your work in the "Calculations" column.

REFLECTING ON WHAT YOU'VE DONE

1. Discuss the following questions with your lab partners and record your group's responses in your science notebook:

A. What did you observe about the effort force with the different pulley combinations?

B. What happened to effort distance as you changed the pulley systems?

C. What do your data tell you about the relationship between effort force and effort distance?

D. Look at the input work done for each trial. Is it the same or different? Discuss this question with the class.

E. Did the load force change each time? Did the work done to lift the load change each time?

2. On the basis of what you learned in this inquiry, write a definition of "machine" in your science notebook.

GOING UP!

It was May 1854. The World's Fair was being held in New York City. On display were the newest inventions from many countries. The crowds were amazed by the promise of technology.

A crowd gathered around a tall, dignified man in a top hat. He mounted a platform. As people looked on, the platform was slowly raised by a rope that was wrapped around a motor-driven drum.

When the platform had ascended well above the crowd, another figure standing on a landing above the platform suddenly reached out and slashed the heavy rope by which the platform was suspended. The crowd gasped.

The platform dropped— but only by a few centimeters. Then it came to a stop. "All safe, ladies and gentlemen, all safe!" the man on the platform proclaimed.

Elisha Otis demonstrates his "safety elevator" to an astonished crowd.

CORBIS/BETTMANN

This drawing shows how early elevators were used to lift people from one floor to the next in a building.

The man on the platform was Elisha Otis, and he'd just proudly demonstrated his invention— the safety elevator. His device would become the first public passenger elevator. Just three years after this dramatic demonstration, the first public passenger elevator was put into service at a New York City department store. By 1873, more than 2000 Otis elevators were being used in office buildings, hotels, and department stores.

An Elevator Fit for a King

The earliest elevators were little more than lifting platforms. More than 2000 years ago, the Romans described lifting platforms that featured pulleys and rotating drums. The power for these devices was supplied by humans or animals. In 1743, France's King Louis XV had a private elevator built in his palace at Versailles. It was operated using human power. Servants pulled on ropes to lift and lower the king. Counterweights helped balance the weight of the king as he moved from floor to floor.

These early elevators had a simple design. The car was suspended by a rope or cable that ran over a pulley at the top of the elevator shaft. At the other end of the cable was a counterweight that balanced with the weight of the car plus the average weight of the load the elevator carried. The car and the counterweight were guided between rails to keep from swinging freely.

Putting on the Brakes

Beginning in 1830 or so, freight elevators were in common use. But all these elevators, including the one used by King Louis XV, had a big drawback: If the rope from which they were suspended snapped, the elevator went crashing to the ground. There was nothing to cushion or stop its descent.

That's why Otis's invention was so important. His safety elevator had something that none of the earlier models did—a brake. If the rope broke, a large spring forced two large latches to lock into ratchets on the guide rails. These latches kept the elevator from falling.

New Forms of Power

The earliest passenger elevators were powered by steam engines. As years passed, other power sources were used. Water pressure was tried. The invention of electric-powered elevators, like Otis's safety device, was an important advance in elevator technology.

The invention of the electric-powered elevator for passengers had a strong effect on city living. Before it came into use, most buildings were no more than four stories high. People just couldn't huff and puff their way up any more flights of stairs! The lack of appropriate building materials was another drawback to the growth of tall buildings.

This elevator was used in about 1900 to carry miners to the pits far below ground.

Changing the Landscape—And People's Lives

By the beginning of the 20th century, the word "skyscraper" had entered the English language. Buildings were built taller and taller—and, thanks to elevators, people could make their way easily to the top. Additional refinements included self-opening doors, an automatic leveling feature, and faster speeds. Modern elevators travel up to 600 meters a minute.

Today, you can zoom to the top of the Washington Monument or the Empire State Building and back in minutes, thanks to electric-powered elevators. And, thanks to Elisha Otis, you can be assured of a safe trip in both directions. ☐

QUESTIONS

1. How are pulleys used in elevators?
2. What is the purpose of the counterweight in an elevator?
3. What has been the impact of elevators on building design?

CORBIS/THE PURCELL TEAM

Safe elevators made living and working in tall buildings practical.

13

The Lever

U.S. gymnast Dominique Dawes performed on the balance beam at the 1996 Summer Olympic Games in Atlanta, Georgia. Her team won a gold medal.

AP/WIDE WORLD PHOTOS

INTRODUCTION

Have you ever played on a seesaw, or used a bottle opener or a fishing pole? If so, you have used a lever. In Lessons 11 and 12, you learned how inclined planes and pulleys work. In this lesson, you will investigate how levers work to balance and lift loads.

OBJECTIVES FOR THIS LESSON

Learn how levers work.

Balance loads on a lever.

Determine the relationship between effort force and effort distance for levers.

Communicate what you learn about levers to others.

Getting Started

1. Discuss the following question with your class: What does it mean to balance something?

2. Draw a picture of something that is balanced and share your drawing with the class.

3. Describe how you could use a lever to lift a rock out of the ground. Draw a diagram showing how to do this. What are the important parts of the lever in your diagram?

MATERIALS FOR LESSON 13

For your group

- 1 pegboard assembly
- 1 pegboard lever
- 1 pegboard bracket
- 1 K'NEX® sled (from Lesson 12)
- 8 large paper clips
- 8 large washers
- 1 piece of masking tape
- 1 0- to 10-N spring scale
- 1 meterstick
- 1 piece of string

Inquiry 13.1
Balancing a Lever

PROCEDURE

1. Have your science notebook ready so you can record your data and answers in it.

2. Set up the pegboard and lever as shown in Figure 13.1.

Figure 13.2 *Washers connected with paper clips*

Figure 13.1 *Pegboard and lever setup*

4. Hang four washers and paper clips three holes from the left of the pivot point, as shown in Figure 13.3.

3. In this inquiry, you will hang washers on the arms of a lever and balance the lever. Figure 13.2 shows how to connect washers with paper clips when hanging them on the lever arm. Use a paper clip on each washer.

Figure 13.3 *Four washers suspended three holes away from the pivot point*

5. When the four washers and paper clips are on the left as shown in Figure 13.3, why doesn't the lever balance? Put four washers on the right side so that they balance the lever. Where are the washers on the right located?

6. Remove the four washers on the right. Leave the four washers on the left. Put three washers somewhere on the right to balance the four washers on the left. Where did you put them?

7. Try balancing other combinations of washers. In your science notebook, make a table to record your results.

8. What factors determine whether two sets of washers will balance a lever? Support your answer with evidence from your data.

9. What general rule can you think up to describe how to balance washers on a lever? Write your rule in your science notebook.

Inquiry 13.2
Lifting a Sled With a Lever

PROCEDURE

1. In this inquiry, you will use a lever to raise your sled. Set up the pegboard assembly with lever, sled, spring scale, and meterstick, as shown in Figure 13.4. The sled should be attached at the end of the lever. (Be sure to zero the spring scale when holding it upside-down since that is how it is used in this inquiry. If the scale has been calibrated right-side up and is then used upside-down, the results will be in error.) As you perform this inquiry, record your measurements on a student sheet or in your science notebook as directed by your teacher.

2. Measure a distance from the tabletop to 0.10 m above the table on the edge of the pegboard where the sled is attached and place a piece of masking tape there (see Figure 13.4). This marks the *load distance*—the distance the sled will be lifted each time.

3. Measure the force the lever must exert to lift the load.

Figure 13.4 *Setup for lifting the sled with the lever*

4. You will investigate the relationship between the effort force you exert to raise the sled and the effort distance—the distance you pull the spring scale. It is important to measure the effort distance and effort force accurately (see Figure 13.5).

Load force

Load distance

Effort distance

Effort force

Figure 13.5 *Effort distance and effort force when using the lever*

5. Attach the spring scale at the end of the lever on the opposite side from the sled.

6. Pull on the spring scale and raise the sled 0.10 m. Observe the force reading on the spring scale as you use the lever to lift the sled. Record the effort force and the effort distance in Table 1 on your student sheet.

7. Attach the spring scale at different positions from the pivot point. Measure and record the effort distance and the effort force to raise the sled 0.10 m each time.

8. What happens to the effort force as the distance of the spring scale from the pivot point changes? Answer this question in your science notebook. Then discuss it with your classmates.

REFLECTING ON WHAT YOU'VE DONE

1. Answer the following questions in your science notebook:

A. On the basis of the results of this lesson, describe how you would balance two sets of washers on a pegboard lever.

B. Was the amount of work done by the lever when it lifted the sled the same each time or different? Explain your reasoning.

C. How did the work you did each time compare with the work done on the sled by the lever?

D. Do you agree or disagree with the following statement: The lever is another example of a simple machine. Cite evidence to support your answer. Discuss your answer to this question with the class.

2. With the class, discuss the advantages and disadvantages of using levers.

UNDERSTANDING LEVERS
AS EASY AS 1·2·3

A lever is one of the handiest tools you will ever find. With a lever, a child weighing 200 newtons can do as much work as a weight lifter who weighs 1000 newtons.

People have used levers for thousands of years. They have always been amazed by their power. In fact, the Greek inventor Archimedes once said, "Give me a lever long enough, and I could move the world."

Of course, he was joking. No one could manufacture a lever big enough to lift the planet. Nevertheless, levers are used every day for hundreds of purposes.

A lever is a simple machine. There are three kinds of levers—first-class, second-class, and third-class. Learning about them, you could say, is as easy as 1, 2, 3.

First-Class Levers: Go Ahead, Pry!

If you've ever ridden a seesaw, you've experienced the power of a first-class lever. A seesaw is a simple lever. The board pivots on a center stand, or

AP/WIDE WORLD PHOTOS

A seesaw is one example of a first-class lever.
Where is the pivot point (fulcrum) for this lever?

fulcrum. The board goes up or down, depending on how much weight is on each end and on the position of these weights.

Suppose your 18-year-old brother is on one end of the board. He weighs about 900 newtons. You're on the other end. You weigh about 500 newtons. Even if your brother weighs 400 newtons more than you, you can lift him on the seesaw just by sitting on the far end of your side of the board. This is because the seesaw acts as a lever. It multiplies the effort that you supply to lift the load (your brother).

Levers such as the seesaw, in which the fulcrum lies between the load and the effort, are called "first-class" levers. With these levers, you exert a force in the opposite direction from where you want the load to move: In other words, to make your brother move up, you must push down.

Second-Class Levers: Hoisting a Heavy Load

A wheelbarrow is a good example of a second-class lever. In this case, the load is between the effort and the fulcrum, which is the wheel. With a second-class lever such as a wheelbarrow, you exert a force in the same direction as the force that does the work (a big difference from the seesaw).

Suppose that your next-door neighbor is doing some landscaping. He's already put three 25-kilogram bags of gravel in his wheelbarrow. The bags weigh a lot—740 newtons! Now he asks you to give him a hand and bring the bags to him. No problem! You walk over to the wheelbarrow and lift the handles, and the load moves up, too. You give a push and you're rolling. The wheelbarrow, which acts like a second-class lever, enables you to lift the 740-newton load by exerting an upward force much smaller than 740 newtons.

Third-Class Levers: Goin' Fishing

When you use a third-class lever, you can move a load a large distance by exerting a big force over a small distance. That's because these levers amplify distance.

A fishing pole is an example of a third-class lever. The fulcrum is close to the handle—near you. The effort exerted by your hand is used to pull the fish from the water. You can lift the load several meters without moving your hand more than a few centimeters or so. Good news for you, not-so-good news for the fish. ☐

QUESTIONS

1. Think about the following list of everyday devices. Be prepared to discuss what type of lever each one is and to identify the fulcrum, the load, and the effort.

   crowbar
   claw hammer
   pliers
   bottle opener
   nail clippers
   pull-open cap
     (on aluminum soda can)
   tweezers

2. How do first-class, second-class, and third-class levers differ?

3. Give an example of each class of lever.

DAVID HISER/PHOTOGRAPHERS/ASPEN/PNI

Opposite: *A wheelbarrow uses the principles of second-class levers to make moving a load easier. Where is the pivot point (fulcrum) for this lever?*
Top: *Fishers take advantage of the principles of a third-class lever to pull fish out of the water. Where is the fulcrum for this lever?*
Left: *Arms are third-class levers. Where are fulcrums for these levers?*

ALEXANDER CALDER:
Making Art Move

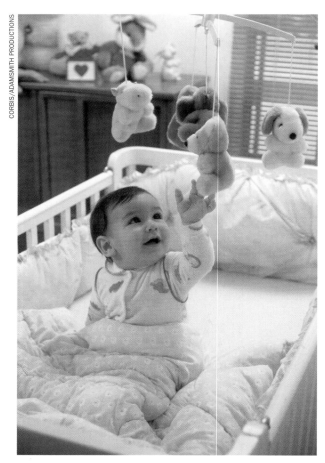

This mobile, moving in the breeze, captures even a baby's attention.

Mobiles are common today—you might see one suspended above your baby sister's crib. But Calder was the genius who first created them.

A good mobile must be beautiful, but it must also balance. This requires engineering skills as well as artistic ability.

First, the beauty. Calder's inspiration was the work of another artist, Piet Mondrian, whose paintings often featured brightly colored squares and black lines. When Calder saw Mondrian's canvases, he said he wanted to make them move.

If you believe that artists and scientists are two totally different kinds of people, you need to know about one of the most famous American sculptors of the 20th century. His name was Alexander Calder. Among his best-known creations are mobiles—moving sculptures made of wood, metal, or other materials, connected by wire, and suspended in the air.

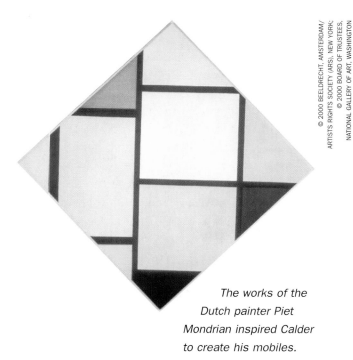

The works of the Dutch painter Piet Mondrian inspired Calder to create his mobiles.

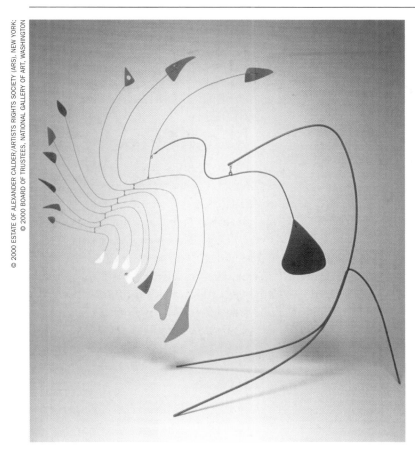

Alexander Calder at work on a sculpture. In all, Calder created 16,000 works of art.

Calder created many kinds of mobiles. Not all of them were suspended from ceilings.

Calder's first mobiles were made of wood, clay, and other objects. Many of his early mobiles needed some help to keep them moving; as a result, they were built with cranks or motors.

But motors were unpredictable—and noisy! Calder decided to construct mobiles that moved naturally—with air currents. He began to use metal and other lighter materials to build his beautiful, airy creations. Some of these beautiful structures are enormous—the one in the atrium of the National Gallery of Art in Washington, D.C., for example, is more than 9 meters high and 23 meters wide.

Calder built his mobiles in different ways. Sometimes he started by attaching two objects to a rod and finding the balance point. Once he found the first balance point, he attached a wire at that spot. He then attached more rods with objects and again found the balance point. Sometimes the mobile got quite complicated!

Other times, Calder started with the pieces. He arranged them in an order that he thought was beautiful. Then he cut and trimmed the pieces until they balanced.

Calder was an artist throughout his life. He began as a child by designing jewelry. Later, he created a mechanical circus made of wire and cork. He continued to make pieces for his circus throughout his life. ☐

QUESTIONS

1. How do you make a mobile?
2. Describe a mobile you have seen. How many pieces did it have? Did it have a theme or main idea?

14

The Mechanical Advantage of Machines

The mechanical advantage of a pulley system makes it possible for these men to lift an overturned truck.

INTRODUCTION

In Lessons 11 through 13, you investigated three kinds of simple machines. You saw that machines make work easier by reducing the effort force needed to do the work. Is one machine better than another? How can you compare different machines? And does the same machine work equally well under different conditions? In this lesson, you will explore these questions and learn one way to compare machines. In Lesson 15, you will learn another way to compare them.

OBJECTIVES FOR THIS LESSON

Calculate the ideal mechanical advantage of inclined planes and pulley systems.

Calculate the actual mechanical advantage of inclined planes and pulley systems.

Compare actual and ideal mechanical advantage.

Getting Started

1. Suppose someone asked you, Which is the best machine: an inclined plane, a pulley, or a lever? Answer the question in your science notebook. Explain how you would decide which is the better machine. Be prepared to share what you wrote with the class.

2. Read "Mechanical Advantage," on pages 132–133.

3. In your science notebook, describe the difference between ideal and actual mechanical advantage.

4. Discuss with the class why someone would want to know the mechanical advantage of one machine over another.

MATERIALS FOR LESSON 14

For you

Your copy of Student Sheet 11.2: What Is the Work Done Using an Inclined Plane?

Your copy of Student Sheet 12.1: How Is a Pulley System Used To Do Work?

1 copy of Student Sheet 14.1: The Mechanical Advantage of Machines

MECHANICAL ADVANTAGE

One way to compare machines is to calculate their mechanical advantage. A machine has two kinds of mechanical advantage—ideal and actual. What is the difference? Ideal mechanical advantage tells how much the machine *increases the effort distance* when doing work. Actual mechanical advantage tells how much the machine *reduces the effort force* when doing work, as shown in the following example.

Suppose a machine has an ideal mechanical advantage of 4.0. What does that mean? It means the effort distance needed to raise a load must be 4 times greater than the load distance. As you know, the load distance is how high you want to lift an object—a sled, for example. If you wanted to lift the sled 0.10 meter, you would have to exert an effort force over a distance of 0.40 meter.

Now suppose that same machine has an actual mechanical advantage of 3.0. That means it would take 4.0 newtons of force to lift a load that weighs 12.0 newtons. Another way to describe actual mechanical advantage is to say that the machine increases effort force by a factor of 3.

Mechanical advantage is based on what you learned in the previous lessons: Machines reduce effort force and increase effort distance. In this example, the actual mechanical advantage is less than the ideal mechanical advantage calculated for the same machine. Can you think of a reason why?

As earlier investigations showed, machines can be set up in different ways. Each setup has two kinds of mechanical advantage—ideal and actual. In this lesson, you will calculate the ideal and actual mechanical advantage for different setups of the inclined plane and the pulley systems that you made in Lessons 11 and 12. To accomplish this, you will perform calculations based on the following equations:

$$\text{Ideal mechanical advantage} = \frac{\text{Effort distance}}{\text{Load distance}} = \frac{\text{Effort distance}}{\text{Distance lifted}}$$

$$\text{Actual mechanical advantage} = \frac{\text{Load force}}{\text{Effort force}} = \frac{\text{Sled weight}}{\text{Effort force}}$$

Look at the two illustrations—one of an inclined plane and one of a pulley—for a review of how to measure forces and distances on an inclined plane and a pulley.

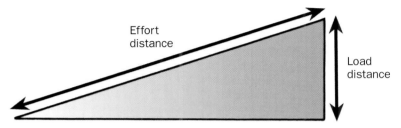

Effort distance and load distance on an inclined plane

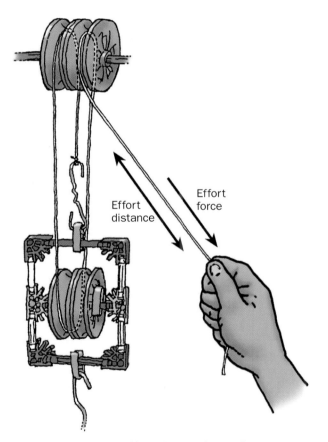

Effort force and effort distance in a pulley system

Inquiry 14.1
Calculating Mechanical Advantage

PROCEDURE

1. Use the effort distance and load distance data you collected in Inquiry 11.2 and recorded on Student Sheet 11.2 (Table 1) to calculate the ideal mechanical advantage for each inclined plane slope. Record your data and calculations in Table 1 on Student Sheet 14.1: The Mechanical Advantage of Machines.

2. Use your effort force and load force data on Student Sheet 11.2 to calculate the actual mechanical advantage for each plane slope. Record your data in Table 2 on Student Sheet 14.1. Then use the blank graph on the student sheet to graph actual mechanical advantage versus slope of the incline.

3. Answer the following questions in your science notebook:

A. Which slope has the largest actual mechanical advantage?

B. Which slope has the largest ideal mechanical advantage?

4. Use the data you collected in Inquiry 12.1 and recorded on Student Sheet 12.1 to calculate the ideal mechanical advantage and the actual mechanical advantage for the pulley systems you assembled. Record your data in Tables 3 and 4 on Student Sheet 14.1.

5. In your science notebook, answer the following questions based on your data for pulleys:

A. Which pulley had the greatest ideal mechanical advantage?

B. Which had the smallest actual mechanical advantage?

C. Why would you want to use a pulley that had a small mechanical advantage?

REFLECTING ON WHAT YOU'VE DONE

Write your answers to the following questions in your science notebook:

A. Examine mechanical advantage for the inclined planes and pulleys. What pattern do you see when comparing ideal mechanical advantage with actual mechanical advantage? How can you explain the pattern?

B. What does actual mechanical advantage tell about a machine's usefulness?

C. You did not calculate mechanical advantage for the levers you studied in Lesson 13. How do you think the ideal and actual mechanical advantages of the lever might compare with those of the pulley and the inclined plane? Explain your reasoning.

Secret Wheelbarrow Technology

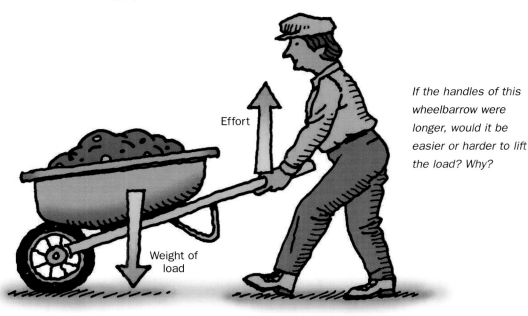

Effort

Weight of load

If the handles of this wheelbarrow were longer, would it be easier or harder to lift the load? Why?

The wheelbarrow is not a fancy machine. It is basically a second-class lever. The axle of the wheel is the fulcrum, the lifting effort is applied to the ends of the handles, and the load is in between.

People in Western Europe have used wheelbarrows for at least 700 years. The earliest record of a wheelbarrow's use in Western civilization is found in a stained-glass window of Chartres Cathedral in France, which was built in the early part of the 13th century.

Wheelbarrows at War?

But don't be fooled—wheelbarrows have been around for much longer than this! Wheelbarrows were being used in China at least a thousand years before they appeared in the window of the Chartres Cathedral. In these early years, instructions on how to build them were closely guarded.

Why? Because wheelbarrows were the Chinese military's secret weapon. Some wheelbarrows were used to carry officers; others were used to transport military equipment or food. Armies in China had special "wheelbarrow brigades," much as modern armies have tank brigades. One job of the wheelbarrow brigades was to support armies who were fighting in hilly terrain where other vehicles couldn't go.

The Chinese even used wheelbarrows to protect the foot soldiers from those who were mounted on horses. Hundreds of wheelbarrows were used to make protective barriers around an army camp—much like the settlers in America made a circle of wagons to protect themselves from attack.

Wheelbarrows at Peace

Today, the wheelbarrow has been put to use for peaceful purposes. For example, it is one of the gardener's essential tools. Modern wheelbarrows come in a variety of forms and sizes, each appropriate for a specific task.

Traditional wheelbarrows, which function as second-class levers, are used to haul things like dirt around your yard or bricks around construction sites.

Wheelbarrows that must carry heavy loads are constructed differently. The wheels are farther from the handles, and the load is placed directly over the axle. That means a small effort force can lift a very heavy load.

The wheelbarrow is not fancy. But it has quite a history. So, if you get bored when your mother asks you to wheel the compost around while you're helping out in the garden, just pretend that you're carrying cargo for an ancient Chinese warlord! ☐

Too hard to push? Some Chinese wheelbarrows had sails that helped move them along.

QUESTIONS

1. What class of lever is a wheelbarrow?
2. How have wheelbarrows been used over the centuries? Summarize briefly.

AP/WIDE WORLD PHOTOS

Wheelbarrows can even carry people.

MORE SIMPLE MACHINES:
The Wedge, Screw, and Wheel and Axle

In Lesson 11, you explored the inclined plane, which is one type of simple machine. In Lessons 12 and 13, you learned about the pulley and the lever, two other types of simple machines.

There are six simple machines in all. The other three are the wedge, the screw, and the wheel and axle. Each of them has things in common with the three simple machines you've explored in class. They all can make work easier by reducing the effort force to do a job while increasing the effort distance. A small effort force gets a big result.

The Wedge

Like a lever, a wedge magnifies force. Like an inclined plane, a wedge is used to move one object in relation to another object. But while an inclined plane is used to move an object along a surface, a wedge is used to move an object into, or even through, an object.

A wedge can be used to split wood.

The simplest form of wedge is a chisel. A chisel is one of oldest machines known to humankind.

An ax is a wedge with a handle. Think about what happens, for example, when you use an ax to split a log. If you can supply sufficient force (and that's not easy!), the log will split into two pieces. But what has happened from the viewpoint of physical forces?

The ax blade is a wedge that has two inclined planes (one on each side of the blade). When you hit the log with an ax, the force you exert pushes the blade of the ax into the log. This forces the wood on both sides of the ax up the inclines and results in a large sideways force that pushes the wood apart, bit by bit. Repeat the motion enough times, and you will split the log.

CORBIS/KARL WEATHERLY

Ice climbers rely on wedges to chip into the ice and hold on.

Axes have other uses. For example, ice climbers drive the blade of an ice ax into the ice. The ice moves apart as the ax makes a narrow wedge in it. After that, the ax is held in place by friction and by sharp teeth along the edge of the blade. Climbers use ice axes while they are making their way up a slope. These axes provide a much stronger grip than bare hands do.

The Screw

A screw is an inclined plane wrapped around a cylinder. When you turn a screw, you move material up an incline. A screw can be used to lift an object or to fasten one object to another.

The screw is another example of a simple machine.

A screw magnifies the driving (or lifting) force. It has to be rotated a fair distance before it will move forward a short distance.

Think about what happens when you put a screw into a piece of wood. It takes a lot of turns! That means your small effort force to turn the screw acts through a large effort distance. Each time you turn the screw, it moves a small distance into the wood with a large force.

Screws are versatile. They can even be used to lift water. Archimedes' screw is a famous invention of ancient times. It was used to raise water from wells to irrigate fields. The device consisted of an inclined plane, in the shape of a screw, that is mounted inside a tight-fitting cylinder. When the operator turned a handle at the top of the screw, water could be raised with much less effort than would be required to lift it directly.

Archimedes' screw is still used today. Here an Archimedes' screw moves plastics through a modern recycling plant.

Wheel and Axle

The wheel and axle works like a lever that rotates 360 degrees around a fixed point. The magnification of force occurs because of the

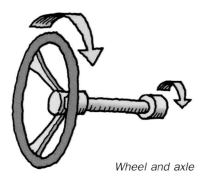

Wheel and axle

difference in size between the wheel and the axle. The larger the wheel compared with the axle, the greater the distance the edge of the wheel moves compared with the edge of the axle. Because the wheel moves a great distance compared with the axle, the force needed to move the wheel is small compared with the force exerted by the axles.

Whenever you turn on a water faucet, you are using a wheel and axle. You apply a small force at the outside of the faucet handle to turn it. This small force creates a larger force on the axle and opens a valve, causing water to flow. Like all machines, the wheel and axle make it possible for a small force to do the work of a large force.

Wheels and axles are used in many other devices, such as can openers, bicycles, and clocks. Some are easy to see; others work behind the scenes. Regardless of whether you see it or not, if machines are turning, wheels and axles are probably at work. □

FOR FURTHER CONSIDERATION
You may want to visit the STC/MS Web site, http://www.stcms.si.edu. There you will find links where you can learn more about simple machines.

Wheels and axles are used to turn valves of all sizes on and off.

15
The Efficiency of Machines

A more efficient train? This train uses magnetic levitation to reduce friction between the train and the tracks. Its sleek design also reduces air friction (drag). Reducing friction enables the train to travel efficiently at high speeds.

INTRODUCTION

In Lesson 14, you learned how to calculate the mechanical advantage of a machine. You found that a machine with a large mechanical advantage can enable a small effort force to lift a heavy load. Does that mean the machine is also efficient? What does it mean for a machine to be efficient? How would you measure efficiency? In this lesson, you will have a chance to learn how efficient your inclined planes and pulleys are.

OBJECTIVES FOR THIS LESSON

Learn to calculate the efficiency of different machines.

Calculate the efficiency of inclined planes and pulley systems.

Compare the efficiency of an inclined plane when the slope of the incline is changed.

Compare the efficiencies of different pulley systems.

THE MEANING OF EFFICIENCY

The word "efficiency" is used to describe the work you get out of a machine compared with the work you put into that machine. An efficient machine puts out a lot of work when compared with the work put into it. On the other hand, if you put a lot of work into a machine and get very little work out of it, then you would say the machine is not very efficient, or it is "inefficient."

To calculate the efficiency of a machine, you divide the output work by the input work, as shown in the following equation:

$$\text{Efficiency} = \frac{\text{Output work}}{\text{Input work}} = \frac{(\text{Load force} \times \text{Load distance})}{(\text{Effort force} \times \text{Effort distance})}$$

Scientists often describe efficiency using percentages; for example, a machine might be described as being "30 percent efficient." That means that the output work is 30 percent of the input work. To calculate efficiency as a percentage, use this equation:

$$\text{Efficiency (\%)} = \frac{\text{Output work}}{\text{Input work}} \times 100\%$$

How does the efficiency of various machines compare? The table below shows the efficiency of different machines, motors, and other things. What is the maximum efficiency that a machine can have? What would that mean? Think about these questions as you work through this lesson.

Efficiencies of Some Common Devices

Item	Efficiency (useful output energy/input energy) (%)
Incandescent lightbulb	5
Automobile engine (gasoline)	25
Nuclear power plant	30
Small electric motor	63

For you
  Your copy of Student Sheet 11.2: What Is the Work Done Using an Inclined Plane?
  Your copy of Student Sheet 12.1: How Is a Pulley System Used To Do Work?
1 copy of Student Sheet 15.1: The Efficiency of Machines

Getting Started

1. Discuss with the class why someone would want to know the efficiency of a machine.

2. Read "The Meaning of Efficiency," on page 141.

Inquiry 15.1
Calculating Efficiency

PROCEDURE

1. You will use the data you collected in Lessons 11 and 12 for this lesson. Use the load force and load distance data that you recorded on Student Sheet 11.2 to calculate the output work when moving the sled up the inclined plane. Enter this measurement into the column for "Output Work" in Table 1 on Student Sheet 15.1.

2. In Table 1 on Student Sheet 15.1, record the input work for four different slopes of the inclined plane. To do this step, use the "Work" column in Table 1 on Student Sheet 11.2.

3. Use the input work and output work information that you have entered in Table 1 and calculate the efficiency of the incline for each slope. Express your answer as a percentage.

4. Answer this question in your science notebook:

What can you conclude about the efficiency of the inclined plane that you used in Lesson 11?

5. Now use the data collected on Student Sheet 12.1 to calculate the efficiency of the pulley systems. Record your calculations in Table 2 on Student Sheet 15.1.

6. Answer this questions in your science notebook:

On the basis of your data for pulleys, which pulley arrangement is the most efficient?

REFLECTING ON WHAT YOU'VE DONE
Answer the following questions in your science notebook. Be prepared to discuss your answers with the class.

A. Examine the efficiencies for the inclined planes and pulleys. Do you see a pattern? How can you explain it?

B. You did not calculate the efficiency for the levers in Lesson 13. What do you think this efficiency would be like? Explain your reasoning.

C. Which would you rather have, a machine with a great mechanical advantage or a machine with high efficiency? Why?

Harnessing the Power of Nature

James Watt and the Steam Engine

James Watt (1736–1819)

During the mid- to late-18th century, workers in Western Europe and America began using power-driven devices in place of hand tools and simple machines. This change in the use of power, known as the Industrial Revolution, had an important impact on people's lives. It was as important as any political upheaval such as the American or French Revolution.

Scientists and inventors played an important part in the Industrial Revolution. Their inventions made major changes in society, which then changed its view of the scientist. No longer was the scientist a natural philosopher and observer; after the Industrial Revolution, the scientist became a public figure whose work affected society.

James Watt represents the link between experimental science and its technological application. Watt's improved steam engine had a major influence on transportation, communication, and industry; thus, it was one of the most far-reaching inventions of the Industrial Revolution.

Watt was born in Scotland in 1736. His education was both classical and practical. He studied Greek, Latin, and mathematics *and* worked on model making in his father's carpentry shop. After an apprenticeship in constructing mathematical instruments such as quadrants, compasses, and scales, Watt opened his own shop in Glasgow. Shortly thereafter, he was able to

examine and test the Newcomen steam engine acquired by the University of Glasgow.

The Newcomen engine, devised by Thomas Newcomen in 1712, used steam—and its expansion and compression—to move a piston back and forth. The piston was connected to a pump that pumped water from coal mines. Newcomen's engine was both primitive and inefficient; it required a large amount of fuel (coal) to generate the steam that drove the piston's motion.

Watt began experimenting with the size of the boiler and its connections to make a more efficient engine. He eventually moved the condensing chamber away from the boiling chamber so that the chambers could be kept hot all of the time. Periodically, Watt had to stop his inventing to return to surveying to earn enough money to support his family. He did, however, secure patents on his improvements and teamed up with a wealthy British merchant, Matthew Boulton, to gain support for his efforts.

Watt's steam engine was a great improvement over the Newcomen engine shown here.

In 1774, after moving to Boulton's manufacturing plant in Birmingham, Watt announced the successful trial of his steam engine. "The fire engine I have invented is now going and answers much better than any other that has yet been made," he said.

Watt continued to make improvements, using improved techniques in tool and metal making, so that his boiler could be made to precise measurements and withstand high pressure. Also, in Watt's engine, the back-and-forth movement of the piston was converted to circular motion. His engine was adopted by Robert Fulton for use in his river steamboat and by Richard Trevithick and George Stephenson in their steam locomotive. The steam engine was used to run machines in factories, especially the textile industry.

During the last years of his life, Watt continued to pursue his scientific interests. He formed the Birmingham Lunar Society. The Society met monthly—on the night of the full moon—so that members could travel home more safely by moonlight on roads that were usually dark. With his Lunar Society colleagues, Joseph Priestley, Erasmus Darwin, and Josiah Wedgwood, Watt discussed scientific phenomena and the study of nature for the good of everyone. Their group firmly believed in progress through the discovery and application of scientific principles.

Steam power is still used today. A train plows through a mountain pass in Colorado.

When James Watt died in 1819, he was recognized as having made significant contributions to science and to the world in his epitaph on a monument to his memory in Westminster Abbey:

James Watt...

...Enlarged the resources of his country,
increased the power of man, and
rose to an eminent place.
Among the most illustrious followers of
science and the real benefactors
of the world.... ☐

QUESTIONS

1. Why was the Newcomen engine inefficient?
2. How did Watt improve the Newcomen engine?
3. Name two people who used Watt's improved steam engine and tell how they used it.

ENERGY STAR®: A Bright Idea

As part of a program called ENERGY STAR®, the U.S. Environmental Protection Agency, the U.S. Department of Energy, and retailers, utilities, manufacturers, and state and local governments are helping Americans save energy, reduce costs, protect the environment, and enjoy the benefits of technology at the same time. These groups educate people about how to use energy efficiently. The companies manufacture energy-efficient products. Products that meet ENERGY STAR® standards receive a special label.

The products approved by ENERGY STAR® are big and small—they include highly energy-efficient refrigerators, lightbulbs, and just about everything in between. The government has given ENERGY STAR®

Appliances and other devices that meet the U.S. Department of Energy's guidelines for energy efficiency display the ENERGY STAR® label.

labels to qualifying computers, dishwashers, air conditioners, furnaces, and electric-powered doors.

Take the lightbulb for starters. Did you know that only 10 percent of the electrical energy used by an incandescent lightbulb becomes light? The other 90 percent is wasted as heat. Halogen bulbs, which burn at temperatures up to 540 degrees Celsius, waste even more energy.

A compact fluorescent bulb (CFL) that has earned the ENERGY STAR® label uses 75 percent less energy than an incandescent bulb, but its light is every bit as bright. CFLs are more expensive than ordinary bulbs, but they last about 10 times longer.

For larger items, the possibilities for savings are

Energy-efficient fluorescent lightbulbs use less energy to produce light. The energy used by one incandescent bulb can light four fluorescent bulbs.

impressive. Refrigerators with the ENERGY STAR® label use 20 percent less electric power than other comparable models. The reason is better insulation and more precise temperature controls. ENERGY STAR®-approved washing machines use only half as much water as standard machines—for a savings of 7000 gallons of water per year in the average household. And when less water is used, there is less water to heat—a second source of energy savings.

Let's not forget the television set. Did you know that it uses energy even when it's turned off? The channel memory and remote control circuits can burn up to 12 watts of power, even when the screen is dark. An ENERGY STAR®-approved TV set, by contrast, uses just 3 watts of power when turned off. That's a 75 percent difference! Multiply that savings by the tens of millions of TVs in homes across America. You can see that ENERGY STAR® can make a difference.

The average American family could reduce its energy bills by about one-third if it bought ENERGY STAR®-rated products to replace existing ones. Office buildings, schools, and other structures can achieve savings as well.

When you go home tonight, you may want to look for the ENERGY STAR® labels on the appliances in your home. Or check out the labels in an appliance store in your area. How many things can you find with the ENERGY STAR® label? ☐

Energy efficiency is not just about making efficient appliances. Insulating houses makes it easier to heat them in the winter and to cool them in the summer, which improves energy efficiency.

16

Machines Assessment: A Technological Design Challenge

Teamwork pays off in the technological design challenge.

INTRODUCTION

In the last several lessons, you have investigated different machines. In this lesson, you will use what you have learned about forces, work, and machines. You will also work on a problem identified earlier in the module. In Lesson 8, you found that the motor alone could not lift the K'NEX® sled loaded with 14 washers. In this lesson, you will be challenged to use a combination of the motor and a machine to lift the sled. To do this, you must design a machine-and-motor apparatus and then build it. You will then evaluate how well your design works. At the end of the lesson, you will share with your classmates the apparatus you designed and built, together with your evaluation of it.

OBJECTIVES FOR THIS LESSON

Develop a solution to a technological design challenge.

Implement your proposed solution.

Interpret data.

Evaluate your solution to the technological design challenge.

Communicate the results of your design solution to others.

Getting Started

1. If you have not done so, read "Science and Technology," on page 150.

2. Answer the following question in your science notebook. Then share your examples with the class.

What are some examples of human needs that can be solved through technology?

3. Review what you have learned about force, work, and machines in this module. Be sure to include mechanical advantage.

4. Discuss with your partners and then with the class why knowing mechanical advantage could help in your machine-and-motor design plans.

5. Make sure you have your student sheets from Lessons 11, 12, 13, and 14 ready to use.

MATERIALS FOR LESSON 16

For you

Your copy of Student Sheet 11.1: Forces on a Cart on the Inclined Plane

Your copy of Student Sheet 12.1: How Is a Pulley System Used To Do Work?

Your copy of Student Sheet 14.1: The Mechanical Advantage of Machines

1 copy of Inquiry Master 16.1: Scoring Rubric for the Technological Design Challenge

1 copy of Student Sheet 16.1a: Planning Our Solution to the Technological Design Challenge

1 copy of Student Sheet 16.1b: Evaluating Our Solution to the Technological Design Challenge

For your group

1 sled (from Lesson 13)
1 pegboard assembly
1 knife switch
1 motor clamp
1 electric motor with wire leads and alligator clips
1 motor pulley with nail
3 large paper clips
3 D-cell batteries
3 D-cell battery holders
3 black insulated connector wires with alligator clips
3 red insulated connector wires with alligator clips
1 0- to 2.5-N spring scale
1 0- to 10-N spring scale
3 machine screws with wing nuts
1 20-cm piece of masking tape
1 2.0-m piece of string
1 meterstick
One of the following:
  1 pegboard lever with pegboard bracket
  1 fixed pulley with 4 pegboard hooks and 1 movable pulley (from Lesson 12)
  1 inclined plane and double loop hook, with wheels for sled
  K'NEX® parts for wheel assembly:
    4 gray connectors (C1)
    2 red rods (R6)
    4 small wheels (W1)

SCIENCE AND TECHNOLOGY

You have conducted many scientific inquiries over the past few weeks. You learned how to control independent variables and how to measure dependent variables. You analyzed your data to discover relationships among the variables. In this lesson, you will do something different. You will design a solution to a technological problem.

How is science different from technology? People often talk about them together, but they are actually different.

Science seeks to discover the basic principles that govern the natural world. It tries to understand and explain the relationships among things. Scientific principles are usually expressed as theories or laws of science. Scientists develop and test their theories by conducting experiments. For example, in previous lessons, you experimented with machines. You learned the basic principles that tell you how machines work. You learned the science behind machines.

Technology, however, tries to meet human needs. Suppose you want to build a machine to do a particular task, such as lifting a load onto a platform. Building a machine is a technological design challenge. First, you must have the necessary materials. Next, you must assemble them to make a working machine. That requires technological understanding of machines and how they work. Based on scientific principles, technological designs create working solutions for people.

In this lesson, you will respond to a technological design challenge that will meet a human need. Your goal will be to build a working model. You must build your device to work within certain design constraints. Work with your teammates and share your ideas. Technological design gives you a chance to combine your creativity and your scientific knowledge.

Inquiry 16.1
Choosing the Machine for the Job

PROCEDURE

1. With your group, review Student Sheet 16.1a: Planning Our Solution to the Technological Design Challenge. The task and specifications for this challenge are described in the Project Brief on the student sheet. You and your fellow engineers will fill out this sheet as you complete your design. The K'NEX® sled with 14 washers is the piano for your model solutions.

2. Read the Project Brief on Student Sheet 16.1a. In your science notebook, answer the questions that follow. Then discuss your answers with the class.

A. What is the human need described in the brief?

B. What will indicate that your design solution is successful?

C. What are the constraints that you must work within when you design your solution?

3. Study the recommended time frame in Table 1: Production Schedule on the student sheet. Discuss this schedule with your team members. Note how much time is suggested for each part of the process. As you move through each step of the design challenge, be sure to record how much time you actually spend on each part.

4. Your teacher will give you a copy of Inquiry Master 16.1: Scoring Rubric for the Technological Design Challenge. Review it with the class.

5. You have worked with three simple machines—the inclined plane, the pulley, and the lever—in previous lessons. Now decide with your teammates which of these machines you will use to build your machine-and-motor apparatus.

6. Work with your team to plan your solution to the design challenge. Be sure to complete the Design Brief on Student Sheet 16.1a: Planning Our Solution to the Technological Design Challenge.

7. Implement your plan by setting up the machine you have selected and connecting it to the motor and batteries.

8. Test your setup. Record the result of the test in your science notebook. Keep in mind the criteria set by the challenge.

9. If the motor did not lift the load, analyze your design, modify it, and try again. Technological designs are often tested and modified to produce the best working model.

10. Evaluate your solution and complete Student Sheet 16.1b: Evaluating Our Solution to the Technological Design Challenge. Answer these questions on the student sheet: How successful were our plan and design ideas? How well were we able to follow our plan? What changes did we make to our original design? How close were we to meeting our proposed time frame as shown in the Production Schedule? In what ways is our final machine-and-motor design different from the design specifications provided? How successful is our final design? If we were to redesign our apparatus, what changes would we make?

TECHNOLOGY—IT'S NOT JUST COMPUTERS

Many people think that the word "technology" refers only to high-speed computers, digitized photography, two-way satellite communication, and the Internet. But technology is not just computers! The pulley, the wheel, and even the pencil are results of technological innovation. These devices have one important thing in common: They have all made life easier.

Although science and engineering are related, each has a different goal. The goal of science is to acquire a systematic knowledge of the world. The goal of engineering is to apply knowledge of science and mathematics in designing products that meet a need. The products might be objects, such as bridges or automobiles, or processes, such as a better way to recycle paper.

Engineers usually begin their work with a set of design requirements. These requirements are based on their expectations for the finished product. The design requirements for an automobile, for instance, might be that it have a maximum speed of 130 kilometers (80 miles) per hour and cost less than $20,000.

Often an engineer will create a prototype, or model, to test whether the final product is likely to meet the design requirements. For example, aeronautical engineers build models of aircraft and test the airflow around them in wind tunnels. Naval architects perform similar tests with models of boats in water tanks. For such tests, engineers create requirements appropriate for the small size of the model. If the model does not satisfy these requirements, the engineers search for ways to improve and modify it. If a particular design continues to fail, it's back to the drawing board! This process of evaluating a design through a repetitive process of testing and refining is the essence of a practice known as technological design.

The design process, in other words, does not always move forward in a predictable way. At any point, an engineering team may have to return to a previous step to make improvements. The design is refined again and again, until the engineers believe they have the best-possible product. In some cases, the finished product may not look anything like what was originally proposed!

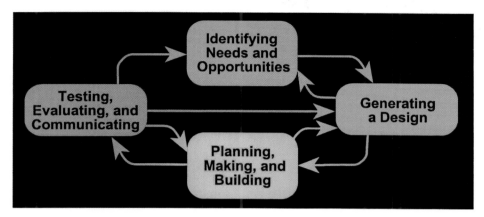

The design technology loop

When do you use the processes of technological design? Almost every time you have to solve a problem. Planning, building, testing, refining, and retesting are the key steps in a cycle that can help you solve just about any problem, from the simplest to the most complex.

REFLECTING ON WHAT YOU'VE DONE

1. As a team, share your solution to the technological design challenge with the rest of the class.

2. On the basis of what you have done in this lesson, discuss with the class how technological design differs from scientific design.

LINKING A COUNTRY TO A CONTINENT

It's only 50 kilometers from Folkestone, England, to Calais, France, but traveling between these two points is harder than you might think. That's because the two cities are separated by the English Channel.

The island country of England has been separated from France and mainland Europe ever since the last Ice Age, some 10,000 years ago. The channel that divides them is not deep, but its waters are choppy. Boat crossings can be rough.

Until recently, the only way to travel from England to France was by boat or plane. Today, however, you can cross the channel by train.

The train goes through a tunnel that was carved out beneath the waters of the English Channel. It is called the Chunnel (short for "Channel Tunnel"). The Chunnel is one of the greatest engineering feats of modern times.

A 300-Year-Old Dream Come True

People have thought about building a tunnel beneath the English Channel for nearly 300 years. In the early 19th century, Emperor Napoleon Bonaparte even had plans drawn up for how it might be done.

Why didn't anything happen? The answer lies in technology. Even though he was the leader of France, Napoleon did not have the equipment or resources to complete such a huge engineering feat. It would have first required drilling through tons of rock. Then all that rock would have to be taken out of the tunnel. Engineers also said they would need to build chimneys that stuck up through the water so that the

CORBIS/HULTON-DEUTSCH COLLECTION

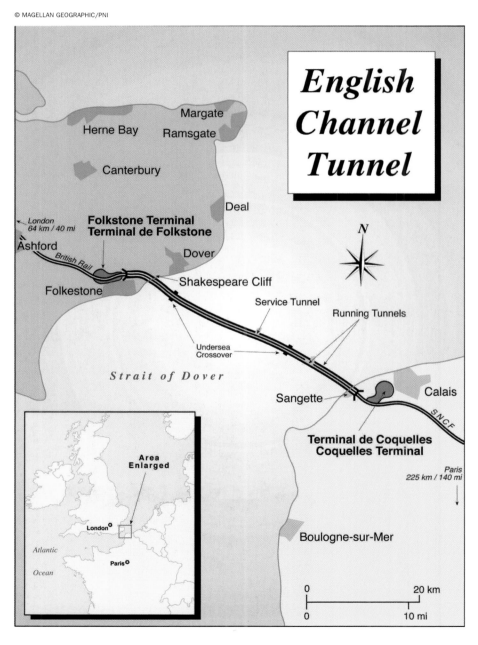

© MAGELLAN GEOGRAPHIC/PNI

Far left: A man emerges from the tunnel dug before the Chunnel was built. Although early attempts to dig a tunnel did not succeed, hopes for a tunnel beneath the English Channel remained alive.

Left: The shallow waters of the English Channel separate France and England.

workers would have air. All in all, it would have been a pretty challenging project.

By the 1870s, drilling machinery had improved. The governments of France and England decided to give the tunnel a try. The French started on their side and the British dug in on the other. The plan was to meet halfway. Each country dug for about a mile and then gave up their shovels. Why? The leaders of the two

Above: *It took huge machines like the one seen here to bore through rock and dirt and create the Chunnel.*
Right: *Today, fast trains such as the one seen here carry people and goods back and forth through the Chunnel.*

It took the cooperation of the governments of France and England, 10 contractors, and the support of 220 banks to make it happen. Workers started to dig on both sides of the channel simultaneously, as they had in the 1870s. This time, however, the effort was much larger. Nearly 250,000 engineering drawings were made. Monstrous machines were used to burrow 50 meters beneath the waters of the channel. The operators had to bore through rock and sediment that were under tremendous pressure from the waters above.

The Chunnel, which opened in 1994, is 50 kilometers long. It accommodates two-way traffic. Its endpoints are Folkestone and Calais, and a one-way trip takes about 30 minutes. Travelers can drive their cars aboard the Chunnel train and remain in them for the crossing. Trucks also ride the train through the Chunnel. Freight trains use the Chunnel to carry goods back and forth between England and the rest of Europe.

The Chunnel is a real success story that shows how technology can be used to meet human needs. People had dreamed of building a tunnel beneath the English Channel for centuries. Technology made it happen. ☐

countries suddenly began to worry about national security. The project was called off.

Making It Happen

Almost a century later, in the 1950s, Frank Davidson, a British attorney, and his wife were crossing from Britain to France on a ferry. The waters were rough, and Mrs. Davidson became seasick. Both of them wished that there was a better way to travel between the two countries.

Mr. Davidson had read about earlier efforts to build a tunnel beneath the waters of the channel. He convinced people in England and France that it was time to try again.

QUESTIONS

1. What human need did the Chunnel meet?
2. What cities are at the ends of the Chunnel?
3. Why did people have to wait until the last half of the 20th century to build a tunnel beneath the English Channel?
4. Explain this statement: Building the Chunnel required the cooperation of many people.

REPORT TO THE PHARAOH

Memorandum

TO: Faruk, Chief Civil Engineer, Giza
FROM: Khufu, Pharaoh of Egypt
DATE: 2600 B.C.
RE: New Work Assignment

I hereby order you to build me a most impressive tomb—a tomb that is truly fit for a king. I want a tomb that will make future generations marvel—a tomb that will last for thousands of years. The site of the tomb will be in the desert at Giza.

I want my tomb to be the tallest building in all Egypt—at least 146 meters high. It must be large enough to house my remains and all my treasures. It also should have chambers for my queen, Henutsen, and for our furniture and other possessions. You must also include secret passageways so that grave robbers cannot steal our treasures.

Please get back to me as soon as possible with your plans for the tomb. How much will it cost? How many workers will be needed? How long will it take to complete the project?

Memorandum

TO: The Honorable Khufu, Pharaoh of Egypt
FROM: Faruk, Chief Civil Engineer, Giza
DATE: 2599 B.C.
RE: Plan for Building The Great Pyramid of Khufu

We are honored that you have requested that we build a tomb to remind future generations of the glory of the reign of the great Pharaoh Khufu.

I have discussed your request with our engineers, designers, and builders. Here are our ideas.

(continu

Building a pyramid takes careful planning.

Page 2, Memo From Chief Civil Engineer

We will begin by consulting the high priests, who will tell us how your pyramid should be positioned. We will then pick the construction site, using the sun and stars to align the sides of the pyramid precisely to the north, south, east, and west. We will level the site and make sure your pyramid has a firm foundation. Each side will be 230 meters long. We estimate that the site will cover about 50,000 square meters.

The pyramid will be built of limestone and granite, which are found in abundance in the desert surrounding Giza. The exterior surface of the pyramid will be made of a smoother rock, which we will mine from a quarry that is about 700 kilometers from Giza on the other side of the Nile River.

My men will use copper and bronze tools to cut the stone. They are hard workers, but you must realize, Your Excellency, that this is a huge job. We will need 2.5 million cubic meters of rock for the basic structure. The workers will cut the rock into 2-ton blocks. To complete this task, we will need thousands of workers.

After the blocks have been cut, they must be moved to the construction site. Because some of the stone will come from across the Nile River, we will need a fleet of barges to float the rock across the river to Giza. For ground transport, we will place the chunks of rock on sleds or rollers and pull them to the building site. But before we can begin to move the rock over land, we will need to construct roadways over which to transport the rocks. Otherwise, the heavy sleds would sink in the sand. You see, Your Excellency, that this is a most complicated project!

(continued)

Page 3, Memo From Chief Civil Engineer

Let us now look at what will happen when the pyramid is under construction. How will we get the rocks up to the top as the pyramid gets higher and higher? At first, we thought of constructing a long ramp or inclined plane. The slope of such a ramp could be no more than 10 degrees. If we wanted to haul rocks to a height of 146 meters at an incline of only 10 degrees, our ramp would have to be 1.5 kilometers long! Since the main quarry is only 300 meters away from the construction site, this would not be practical.

Instead, we propose to wrap the ramp *around* the pyramid—like a spiral staircase. The ramp will be made from mortar and stone chips. We will place wooden ties on the ramp. We will lubricate the ties with wet clay to make it easier for the blocks to slip over them as they are pulled up the side of the pyramid. When the block gets to the spot where it is needed, we will use a lever to move it into place. When the pyramid is finished, we will remove the ramp.

I hope you can understand, Your Excellency, that this project will take many years and millions of hours to complete. We estimate that it will take at least 20 years, maybe more. We are ready to begin when you say the word. We promise that your tombstone will truly be a wonder of the world. ☐

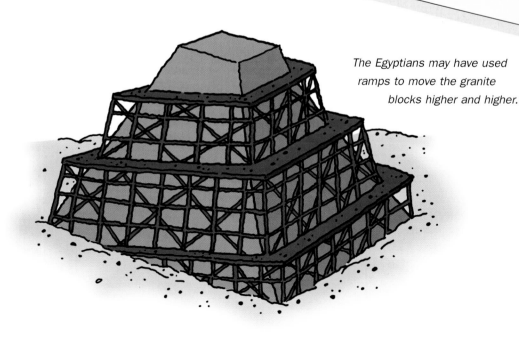

The Egyptians may have used ramps to move the granite blocks higher and higher.

CORBIS/ROGER RESSMEYER

Khufu's Pyramid

More than 4600 years after its construction, Khufu's pyramid, built with simple machines and millions of hours of manpower, stands as a monument to this pharaoh. Until the 19th century, Khufu's pyramid was the tallest building in the world!

CORBIS/KEVIN R. MORRIS

Today, workers build skyscrapers more than 100 stories tall. What machines do they use?

PART 3 Motion

17

Introduction to the Anchor Activity

This shoe-testing machine is designed to test leather soles.

INTRODUCTION

In this lesson, you will begin the Anchor Activity, a research project that will give you the opportunity to apply what you have learned in this module to a new situation. You and your partner will select a single device to study. Or, if you wish, you may design and build your own device. Whichever option you choose, you will do research to obtain as much information as you can about this device during the next few weeks. You will focus on how this device demonstrates the concepts and principles of energy, machines, and motion that you have studied. During the last lesson of this module, you will demonstrate to the class how your device works and share what you have learned about it.

OBJECTIVES FOR THIS LESSON

Understand the goals of the Anchor Activity.

Select a device to research or build.

Develop a plan to research or build the selected device.

Getting Started

1. Read "Civil Engineering: Danelle Bernard's Bridge to the Future," on pages 168–170.

2. Participate in a class discussion about what you have read.

3. Discuss with the class the importance of working together as a team.

Inquiry 17.1
Beginning the Anchor Activity

PROCEDURE

1. Participate in a class discussion of the purpose and goals of the Anchor Activity.

2. To get started, you need to come up with some ideas for devices that you can research. With the class, brainstorm the kind of devices you could investigate. You may suggest existing devices or devices you could design and build. Suggest any ideas that come to mind. Do not judge an idea right now. Do not worry if it is a good or bad idea. You will decide that later. You want to make a list of as many ideas as you can.

**MATERIALS FOR
LESSON 17**

For you

1 copy of Student Sheet 17.1a: Guidelines for the Anchor Activity: Investigating a Device That Is Already Made

1 copy of Student Sheet 17.1b: Guidelines for the Anchor Activity: Making a Device of Your Own

1 copy of Student Sheet 17.1c: Getting Started on the Anchor Activity

1 copy of Inquiry Master 17.1c: Calendar for the Anchor Activity

3. With the class, evaluate each device on the list. Some devices will be reasonable to research; others will not. Your teacher will delete from the list any devices that will not work.

4. With your partner, decide on the device you would like to investigate or build. If you would like to investigate or build a device that is not on the list, check with your teacher to be sure that it is acceptable. Remember, it should be something that you can use. It must also be safe to use and demonstrate at school.

5. In your science notebook, record the device you choose.

6. Your teacher will give you a student sheet that lists Anchor Activity guidelines for your chosen device. Follow along as your teacher reviews each part of the project. Make sure you understand what is expected for each part. Ask questions about anything that is not clear.

7. Now review the calendar on Inquiry Master 17.1c. It tells you the dates by which each part of your project should be completed. Put the Anchor Activity guidelines and the calendar in the front of your science notebook so you can refer to them later. Be sure to follow the calendar so that you complete everything on time and receive full credit for your work.

8. Discuss with your lab partner where you think you can find information about your device. Share your ideas with the rest of the class.

9. Complete Student Sheet 17.1c: Getting Started on the Anchor Activity.

10. Read "How To Succeed With Your Project," on the next page.

HOW TO SUCCEED WITH YOUR PROJECT

Research takes time and succeeds with steady, continuous effort. Your final grade for the Anchor Activity will be the sum of all the scores earned throughout the project, not a single grade given at the end. To earn the most credit, complete each part on time and follow directions.

You will complete the Anchor Activity over the next few weeks. You will do most of the work for it outside the classroom. Sometimes you will work on your own. At other times you will work with your lab partner at home, at school, or at the library. If you live near your lab partner, you will have opportunities to meet outside of school time to complete your research and design your presentation. Some class time will be given for working on the project. Make good use of it. It gives you a chance to ask any questions you may have.

A good plan of action will also help you complete the project. Your plan should include not only what you and your partner will do, but also when and where you will meet to complete your research and design your presentation. In addition to a plan, you will need a calendar with a schedule for completion of the project. Setting deadlines for different parts of the Anchor Activity makes it less likely that you will have to do a lot of work at the last minute.

Keep a log or journal of your work in your science notebook. The log should tell what you did to contribute to the group effort and when you did it. Record your thoughts and ideas as you work. You may want to have your parents sign your log. This shows you have been working steadily on the project.

Information comes in many forms. Learn to use all the different resources at your school or local library. Your teacher may arrange for you to go to your school library or computer lab to do some of your research. Librarians and computer resource teachers can help you find information and plan your presentation.

Think of different ways you can share what you learned. Putting the information on a poster is one way; using computers is another. Your teacher will give you information about how to plan your presentation. Choose the format that best fits the resources in your school.

Plan and practice your oral presentation. A well-organized presentation is the best way to get your information across. It will earn you the most credit.

CIVIL ENGINEERING

Danelle Bernard's Bridge to the Future

PHOTO BY MARVIN D. BLIMLINE/MARYLAND STATE HIGHWAY ADMINISTRATION

Danelle Bernard

"When I was in high school," recalls Danelle Bernard, "I really liked math, science, and physics. I also was interested in architecture. For a while I thought about becoming an architect. But then I decided I wasn't 'artsy' enough."

Danelle's guidance counselor gave her a good idea. "Why not think about becoming a civil engineer?" he asked.

Danelle looked into civil engineering and soon decided that it was the career for her. She graduated from college with a bachelor of science degree in civil engineering. Her courses covered topics such as design of steel structures, design of concrete structures, soil mechanics, surveying, structural analysis, and construction cost estimating. After working for 4 years, Danelle took a test that qualifies those who pass it as

licensed professional engineers. Many employers require licensing, which is like a degree.

Today, about 15 years after graduation, Danelle is a project engineer for the Bridge Design Division, which is part of the State Highway Administration in Maryland. Danelle and her coworkers have a big responsibility: to oversee the design of bridges throughout the state. The group is responsible for designs aimed at repairing old bridges (some of which are almost 100 years old) as well as building new ones. Some of the bridges are quite small. "They're out in the middle of a cornfield," she says with a smile. Many others, however, are large, concrete-and-steel structures located in urban areas. Thousands of vehicles pass over them every day. At any moment, Danelle and her group are working on about a dozen projects. Each takes about 1 to 2 years to complete.

Teamwork

One thing Danelle likes best about her job is that it involves teamwork. Several different groups of people, composed mainly of engineers, work on Maryland's bridges. One group, for example, is in charge of inspecting all of the state's bridges. Maryland has more than 2400 bridges, and federal law requires that each bridge be inspected every 2 years.

PHOTO BY MARVIN D. BLIMLINE/MARYLAND STATE HIGHWAY ADMINISTRATION

Bridge maintenance is the job of civil engineers.

The inspection teams examine the bridge carefully. If they see cracks or other signs of deterioration, the bridges are slated for repair work. The bridge inspection group has several teams of engineers who do the design for minor bridge repairs. If a bridge requires major repairs or has to be replaced because it is severely deteriorated, however, it is turned over to the Bridge Design Division, which includes Danelle's team.

The bridge design team carefully analyzes the forces acting on the bridge. Their objective is to determine how strong the structural members of the bridge have to be to carry the weight of the vehicles that will pass over it. They must make sure that the bridge meets national and state design codes, but at the same time they have to think about cost constraints. When you've got more than 2400 bridges to think about, saving money is important!

Protecting the environment is also a concern. When a new bridge is being designed or an existing bridge is being repaired, Danelle and her team often meet with local citizens, elected officials, and members of environmental groups to discuss the effect that the bridge will have on the local community and the environment.

After Danelle and her colleagues have figured out all the details related to the bridge design, it's time to bring in the drafters, who transfer the designs into plans that will be used to build the bridge. In the past, drafting was much more painstaking. A lot of time was spent drawing, erasing, and drawing again! Today's drafts-persons use CADD, short for "computer-aided drafting and design," to create the bridge plans. Changes can be made much more easily. In fact, using CADD, the drafters can even superimpose a drawing of a bridge onto a photograph

Using computer technology to redesign bridges

to show how a new bridge will look in a certain area. That comes in handy when the bridge design team is working with local residents who are concerned that the bridge will destroy the appearance of their neighborhood.

Always Something Different

Why is Danelle so enthusiastic about her work? There are many reasons. The first is simple—it's a job that is definitely needed. "Bridges help people get to work, get around, and do what they need to do!" she exclaims. Another big advantage is that you can see the results of your work.

"Every time I drive on the highway," she says, "I can say to myself, 'I helped design that bridge.' "

The third reason is that every day brings new challenges. "Every bridge is different," she says. "Every project goes differently. We don't just sit at a desk and 'crunch numbers.' We get involved with local citizens and people from diverse backgrounds. And when the bridge is under construction, we go out and meet with the construction crews. You're gaining new experience all the time. It's something that you could never learn from a textbook." □

HOW TO DO A SIMPLE TASK—IN JUST 13 STEPS

Rube Goldberg began his career as a cartoonist in 1904.

Imagine making a pencil sharpener that also peels oranges. Sounds pretty weird, doesn't it? But that's the kind of thing that happens across the country each year in the Rube Goldberg Machine Contest™ held at various high schools, colleges, and universities. Teams of students compete to make machines that combine multiple steps and assorted gadgets to complete simple tasks such as sharpening pencils, toasting bread, and wiping chins.

Who was Rube Goldberg? He was an American cartoonist whose specialty was poking fun at the unnecessary complications of modern technology. He was born in San Francisco, California, in 1883. His cartoons showed complicated devices for doing a simple job. The "chin-wiper" pictured here is a typical Rube Goldberg machine. It takes 13 steps for the self-operating napkin to work. Why would anyone think of a machine like this?

During the decades that Rube Goldberg's work was featured in the nation's media, technological inventions were changing life dramatically. New devices, such as the telephone and washing machine, allowed people to use services for which they formerly needed to hire someone. In the early part of this century, these devices made people a little nervous (just like

This Rube Goldberg™ device—The Self-Operating Napkin—combines practical and whimsical elements.

computers and pagers make some people nervous today!). Rube Goldberg's drawings of far-fetched machines completing easy tasks became so popular that Americans now associate the phrase "Rube Goldberg machine" with any system that seems too complicated.

Pails, Paddles, and Scientific Principles

Rube's machines used everything from false arms to wheels, cups, rods, paddles, pails, kitchen tools, and old shoes. But these devices, no matter how extravagant, did demonstrate a keen knowledge of physics. Rube's father insisted that his son earn a technical degree

before embarking on a career as an artist. While a graduate engineering student, Rube learned most of the principles that make his creations tick. It's no wonder that his designs are popular with engineering students—and they were the ones who began hosting the Rube Goldberg Machine Contest in the 1930s.

Today, the Rube Goldberg Machine Contest is held all over the United States. The largest and oldest is hosted by Pi Theta Tau, the engineering society at Purdue University in Lafayette, Indiana. Student finalists have appeared with their machines on late-night television talk shows and in many magazine and newspaper articles.

BALLOONS MAY BE MADE REALLY USEFUL.
BIG IDEA FOR WESTERN RAILROADS! HOW THEY MAY SAVE THEIR PASSENGERS FROM REAR-END COLLISIONS AND THEMSELVES FROM HEAVY SUITS FOR DAMAGES!

Rube Goldberg was not the only artist of his time to poke fun at modern technology. This railroad car is designed to protect passengers from train collisions.

AP/WIDE WORLD PHOTOS

The 1999 Rube Goldberg Machine Contest winners with their Rube Goldberg devices

The Contest Rules

All competitions have rules, and the Rube Goldberg Machine Contest is no exception. Some of the rules that usually apply to high school competitions are the following:

- Machines must operate within the following dimensions: 5 feet high, 6 feet wide, and 5 feet deep.
- Machines must complete one cycle of all steps within 9 minutes.
- Machines cannot have any loose or flying objects (for example, drops of water, confetti, and feathers) fall outside their established boundaries.

Once judges have determined that an entry passes these guidelines, the machine is judged for creativity, efficiency, and "Rube Goldberg" spirit. Every machine must have a theme—these range from *Star Wars* to the everyday (for example, junk food and housekeeping).

The 1998 competition prize was captured by a team from the University of Texas at Austin, whose "Mission to Mars/Spaceship Goldberg" took a combination of 40 steps—mechanical, electrical, and chemical—to turn off an alarm clock. It began with a solar-powered clock knocking down a weight and ended with a miniature model of the Mars Sojourner Rover roaring down a track, dropping a curtain over the clock, and turning it off. It's complex—but it works! □

18

Motion of a Fan Car

The assembled fan car

INTRODUCTION

You will now begin the first of four lessons in which you will investigate the relationship of force, motion, and energy. In this lesson, you will study the motion of a fan car that you construct using K'NEX® parts and a battery-powered fan. You will observe the motion of the fan car with the fan turned off and with the fan turned on. In Lesson 19, you will study the motion of a vehicle powered by a mousetrap. Then, in Lessons 20 and 21, you will build a model roller coaster and study the motion of a car moving on the roller coaster. As in previous lessons, you will make predictions, record observations, gather data, and draw conclusions based on evidence from your observations and data.

OBJECTIVES FOR THIS LESSON

Describe the force exerted by a battery-powered fan.

Describe the motion of a fan car.

Determine the effect of a constant force on the speed of a fan car.

Calculate a fan car's average speed at different times as it moves along a path.

Getting Started

1. Read "Measuring Motion" on page 177. What does the term "average speed" mean? How do you calculate it? Discuss these questions with the class.

2. Solve the following two exercises to practice calculating average speed.

A. A car travels 100 meters (m) in 2 seconds. What is its speed?

B. A jogger runs 50 meters in 25 seconds. What is the jogger's speed?

3. Assemble the fan car as shown in Figures 18.1 and 18.2. (Your teacher will provide the batteries later in the inquiry.) Figure 18.1 is an exploded diagram, which shows you the parts needed to make the fan car. Figure 18.2 shows how the parts look in the completed car. Your teacher has a model that you can also examine.

4. When you are finished, your car should look like the one in the photo at the beginning of this lesson. Check to make sure that it does.

MATERIALS FOR LESSON 18

For you

1 copy of Student Sheet 18.2: How Fast Is the Car Going?

For your group

1 fan car
1 battery-powered fan
2 AA batteries
1 rubber band
1 student timer
1 meterstick
1 2.0-m piece of adding machine tape
1 20-cm piece of masking tape

K'NEX® parts for the fan car (see Appendix A: Directory of K'NEX® Parts):

8 gray connectors (C1)
8 red connectors (C4)
8 white rods (R2)
4 blue rods (R3)
1 yellow rod (R4)
3 small wheels (W1)
3 small tires (T1) (optional)

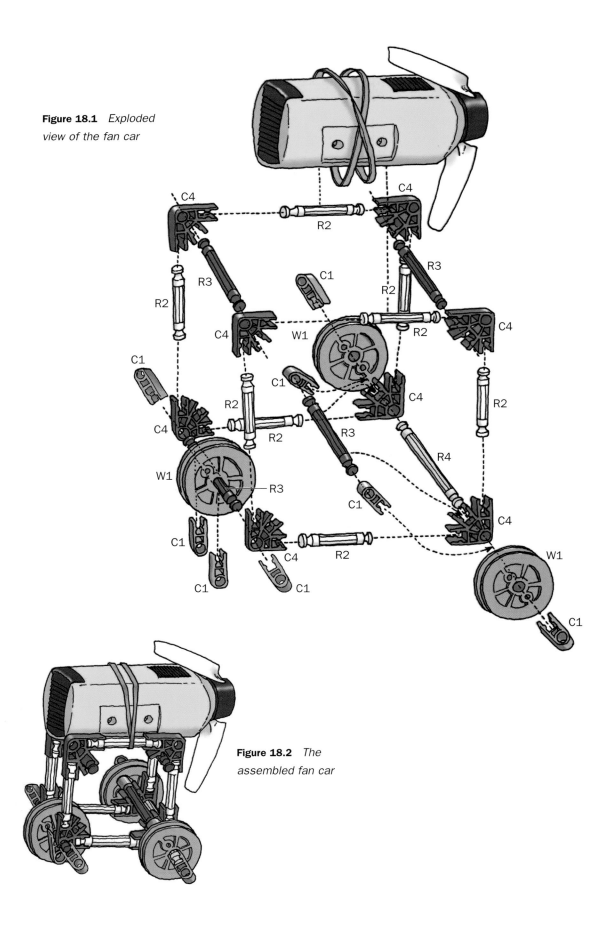

Figure 18.1 *Exploded view of the fan car*

Figure 18.2 *The assembled fan car*

MEASURING MOTION

We see motion everywhere—think, for instance, of joggers, runners, swimmers, cars, and buses, to name just a few examples. Motion is easy to recognize. It can be described with words such as "fast" and "slow." But these words do not describe motion as precisely as scientists like to describe it. How fast is fast? How slow is slow? Fast to one person may seem slow to another. To help deal with these differences, scientists have developed a way to describe an object's motion. They measure or calculate the speed of objects that are moving. When they do that, they can easily compare the motion of fast and slow objects.

What is speed? When something is moving, it is changing its position. It takes time for this change to happen. Speed tells how fast the object changes its position. How do you measure or calculate the speed with which this happens? The speed of an object is calculated as the distance it traveled divided by the time of travel.

The speedometer on a car measures the speed of the car. It tells how far the car travels during a given time period. For example, if the speedometer registers 96 kilometers per hour (60 miles per hour), then the car is changing its position by 96 kilometers every hour. You will travel 96 kilometers each hour you ride in the car.

Is 96 kilometers per hour fast? That depends on how the speed compares with the speed of other things. For example, a jogger may have a speed of 5 kilometers per hour. Compared with the jogger, the car is moving fast. But how does the speed of the car compare with that of a plane moving 800 kilometers per hour? That comparison makes the car seem to be moving pretty slowly.

By using speed to measure the motion of things, we can compare motion in a meaningful way. If the speed of an object varies during a time interval the way the speed of a car does, the total distance traveled divided by the time to travel the distance is called the average speed.

How do you know the speed of objects if they don't have speedometers? You need two measurements. One measurement is how far an object has traveled. The other measurement is how much time it takes to travel that distance. The rate at which the object is changing its position—its average speed—can be calculated using the following equation:

$$\text{Speed} = \frac{\text{Distance traveled}}{\text{Time of travel}}$$

For example, if a car travels 200 kilometers in 4 hours, its speed is 200 kilometers divided by 4 hours, which equals 50 kilometers per hour.

In this lesson, you will use this definition of speed to calculate the speed of a moving fan car. To calculate accurate values for the speed, you will measure the distance traveled with a meterstick. You also need to measure the time it takes the car to travel each distance with a student timer.

Inquiry 18.1
Investigating the Motion of the Fan Car

PROCEDURE

1. Now that you have constructed your fan car, you will make some predictions and observations about its motion with the fan *off*. In your science notebook, design a table to record your predictions and observations as you complete the activities below. Later, you will discuss your predictions and observations with the class.

2. Record your predictions for the motion of the fan car if you push it and release it without the fan running.

3. Now push the fan car. Use a steady push. Record your observations of its motion after you release it.

4. Repeat Step 3 using forces of different strengths.

5. What differences in motion do you see when you change the push on the car? Cite evidence from your observations to support your answer.

6. When you pushed on the car, your hand exerted a force on it. List in your science notebook any other forces that were acting on the car when you pushed it.

7. What force(s) acted on the car after you released it? Record your answer in your science notebook.

8. You will now investigate the motion of the car with the fan on. Put two AA batteries in the fan base. Place the fan car on the table or on another flat surface, hold it in place, and turn on the fan *without letting go of the car.* Both you and your partner should do this. Answer the following questions in your science notebook:

A. What do you feel when you simply hold the car with the fan running?

B. In what direction does the fan move the air?

C. In what direction does the fan car want to move?

9. Before releasing the car, discuss with your partner how you think the fan car will move if you release it with the fan turned on.

10. Now release the car with the fan turned on. Observe and describe its motion in your science notebook.

11. Discuss with your partner how the motion of the fan car with the fan running compares with its motion after you released it with the fan turned off.

SAFETY TIP

Keep your fingers away from the moving fan blades.

Inquiry 18.2
Measuring the Fan Car's Speed

PROCEDURE

1. With the class, review the behavior of the fan car turned off and turned on.

2. In this inquiry, you will measure the motion of the fan car. One way to do this is to measure the speed of the fan car as it moves across the table or floor. Review the information in the reader "Measuring Motion." Find the equation for calculating average speed and write it in your science notebook. You will use this equation in the activities that follow.

3. Place a long piece of adding-machine tape across the tabletop or floor. Use a piece of masking tape to mark a starting point at one end of the adding-machine tape.

4. Beginning at the starting point (0.0 m), mark distances in 0.4-m segments along the adding-machine tape, going all the way to 2.0 m (if possible), as shown in Table 1 on Student Sheet 18.2: How Fast Is the Car Going?

5. Label your tape distances along the tape as shown in Figure 18.3.

6. Accurate timing is important for this inquiry. The times you measure will be very short. Before you begin collecting your data, practice your timing skills. Take turns operating the student timer and see who in your group is best at measuring short time intervals with it. Your teacher will provide an object for you to practice with. Drop the object and measure the time it takes the object to fall to the floor. The best timer is the person who can easily operate the student timer and get very close to the same timings for each drop. The best timer should operate the student timer for your group.

7. Using the student timer, determine the average time it takes the fan car to travel each 0.4-m interval along the tape. Work as a team. It is important to start and stop the student timer at the right instants. Try to keep the car traveling in a straight line along the tape.

8. Use your average time to pass through each 0.4-m interval to calculate the *average* speed of your fan car during the intervals indicated in Table 1 on your student sheet. Calculate and record the speeds in Table 1.

9. What patterns do you observe in your speed data? Answer this question in your science notebook.

10. Follow your teacher's instructions to disassemble your car and return the parts to storage.

Adding-Machine Tape Measurements

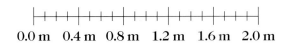

0.0 m   0.4 m   0.8 m   1.2 m   1.6 m   2.0 m

Figure 18.3 *How to mark the tape for measuring average speed of the fan car*

REFLECTING ON WHAT YOU'VE DONE

Answer the following questions in your science notebook. Be prepared to discuss your answers in class.

A. *What are the forces on the fan car when the car is moving with the fan turned off and when it is moving with the fan turned on? What evidence do you have to support your answer?*

B. *Is the force of the fan constant or changing as the car moves along? Give reasons for your answer.*

C. *What is the effect of the force of the fan on the speed of the car? Cite evidence for your answer.*

D. *What can you conclude about the effect of a constant fan force on the motion of the car?*

E. *What energy changes take place as the car moves along with the fan running?*

PROPELLERS:
VEHICLES IN MOTION

In this lesson, you observed the spinning blades of the fan producing a force that moved your fan car. That fan acted like a propeller. Like all propellers, it had a blade that rotated around a central hub. Fan cars aren't the only vehicles that use propellers. Vehicles for air, sea, and land all use propellers. ☐

In Air

Helicopters use their propellers to create a force that lifts them off the ground. By changing the angle of the main propeller, the pilot can make the helicopter move forward. The smaller propeller on the tail of the helicopter creates a force that keeps the body of the helicopter from spinning in circles. Its force can also be used to turn the helicopter.

Many airplanes have propellers. Like the propellers on a helicopter, these propellers are used to move the airplane forward. However, in most planes, the propellers don't directly cause the plane to lift off the ground. The angle of the wings and the air flowing around them lift the plane into the air. But a special kind of plane, called a tilt-rotor plane, has a propeller that can be used like a helicopter's propeller to lift the plane off the ground. When the helicopter is aloft, the propellers can be turned and used like propellers on a regular airplane.

On Water

CORBIS/DAN GURAVICH

Boats, like aircraft, use propellers to move. Many boats use propellers below the surface of the water. These propellers—unlike those on an aircraft and on a fan car—push against water instead of air to move the vehicle forward. Some boat propellers are very big. Notice the size of the propeller compared with the size of the men in this photograph. This propeller was used on a boat that transported oil from Alaska to the East Coast of the United States.

Sometimes underwater propellers can cause problems. In swamps and places like the Everglades, where the water is shallow and where plants grow along the surface, a propeller can get tangled in plants or caught on the bottom. Airboats are designed to solve these problems. Airboats work much the same way as fan cars. A fanlike propeller on the back of the airboat pushes against the air to move the airboat across the surface of the water.

CORBIS/RAYMOND GEBMAN

On Land

CORBIS

Propellers are not used on land vehicles as commonly as they are on air and water vehicles. However, some creative people have designed propeller-powered land vehicles. This snow sled uses a propeller just like the one on your fan car. Because the sled is designed for the snow, it has skis instead of wheels.

In 1931, a propeller was used to move an unusual vehicle along a railroad track. The vehicle, named a railway zeppelin, traveled 269 kilometers (168 miles) at an average speed of more than 160 kilometers (100 miles) per hour. Its highest speed was 230 kilometers (144 miles) per hour.

CORBIS/HULTON-DEUTSCH COLLECTION

Sailing Through the Solar System

Solar sails may take many shapes and use different materials. Cosmonauts tested this circular, shiny blue Znamya solar sail to show that solar sailing may indeed one day be possible.

Scientists and engineers are always looking for ways to improve things. They try to achieve two goals: making things work better and making them cost less. The more complex a project, the bigger the challenge.

From this perspective, one of the biggest challenges is space travel. A great deal of energy is required to send spacecraft into space. Powerful rockets are needed to launch spacecraft and to provide the velocity they need to travel through the solar system. These rockets are expensive. The fuel is expensive, too.

How could space travel be made less expensive? One idea that scientists are exploring is solar power. Some scientists believe that a spacecraft could actually *sail* through the solar system. Solar-sailing spacecraft could travel large distances through the solar system using very little fuel.

On the earth, sailboats use the pressure of the wind.

Sailing Boats on Earth

On the earth, sailboats glide across lakes, oceans, and bays. Sailboats need no fuel. They are powered by the wind. When the force of the wind is greater than the drag (friction) of a sailboat in the water, the wind pushes the boat forward. The navigator speeds the boat up or slows it down by controlling the angle the sails make with the wind. The navigator can also use the force of the wind and the rudder to change the direction the boat is going.

But in space, there is neither air nor wind. So how could a spacecraft *sail*? The answer is this: Spacecraft may be able to sail using the pressure of sunlight.

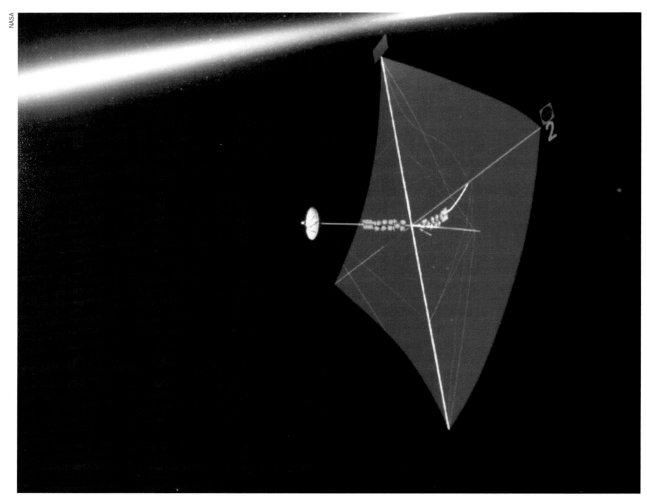

Here is one design for a solar sail. Solar sails will be very large in size but not very massive. Large sails are needed to reflect enough sunlight to create pressure to push the craft through space.

How Solar Sails Would Work

Sunlight is made of tiny energy packets called photons. If light traveling in straight lines out from the sun struck the sails of a spacecraft, the photons would bombard the sail like tiny Ping-Pong balls. When the photons struck the sail, they would push on it with a very small force. Because there is no air friction in space, the spacecraft would sail along with only the pressure of the photons of light and gravity acting on it.

So far, so good. But here's the drawback. A very large force is needed to power something as big as a spacecraft. Photons come in vast quantities, but their individual power is small. One way to increase the force would be to make the sails of the spacecraft larger; in this way, more photons would hit it. But scientists have estimated that to catch enough photons to make a spacecraft move, the sails would have to measure a kilometer on each side. A sail that big would cover about 175 football fields!

More Solutions, Please!

Another way to maximize the force of the photons on the sails would be to make sure the light reflects off the surface of the sails as strongly as possible. This could be accomplished by manufacturing sails from a material that reflects light like a mirror.

Another solution might be to make the sails as lightweight as possible. Scientists and engineers will be challenged to develop and design sails made of ultra-lightweight materials so the spacecraft will have as little mass as possible.

Scientists and engineers are creative. They have many ideas about how to make space sailing work. But on one thing they do agree: Designing huge sails that have very little mass and that are highly reflective is a real technological challenge.

There are no solar-sailing spacecraft yet, but scientists do hope to have them one day. These spacecraft could be placed in positions that would allow them to constantly monitor the earth and the sun. The findings they would transmit could help us better understand weather patterns and climate changes on the earth, as well as storms on the sun. Solar-sailing spacecraft might be able to visit planets, moons, comets, and asteroids and send back exciting new data. Some scientists even hope to use such vehicles someday to send a spacecraft to the stars.

Solar sailing is a dream of the future, but scientists and engineers are working to make it happen. New materials and technologies will be needed. New challenges will be met, and new discoveries made. ☐

19
Motion of a Mousetrap Car

The assembled mousetrap car

INTRODUCTION

In Lesson 18, you built a fan car and measured its speed. In this lesson, you will build a "mousetrap car" and investigate its motion. You will design an experiment that will enable you to measure the speed of the car as it moves after the trap is released. You will also identify the forces acting on the car and describe how these forces affect the car's motion. You will then compare the motions of the fan car with those of the mousetrap car.

OBJECTIVES FOR THIS LESSON

Identify and describe the forces acting on the mousetrap car.

Observe and measure the speed of the mousetrap car as it moves.

Describe how forces affect the motion of the mousetrap car.

Describe the energy changes in the mousetrap car as it moves across the floor.

Compare the motion of the fan car with the motion of the mousetrap car.

Getting Started

1. Assemble the mousetrap car as shown in Figure 19.1; the exploded diagram shows all the parts needed to assemble the car and how they connect. Figure 19.2 shows the car with the pieces properly connected. (The photo at the beginning of this lesson also shows the assembled mousetrap car.) It is important that you use a long piece of nylon line so that the axle will keep rotating after the trap has been released. If the nylon line is too short, it will unwind and then begin winding the opposite way.

MATERIALS FOR LESSON 19

For your group

1 student timer
1 meterstick
1 0- to 10-N spring scale
1 piece of adding machine tape
K'NEX® parts for the mousetrap car (see Appendix A: Directory of K'NEX® Parts):
  6 gray connectors (C1)
  2 tan connectors (C2)
  14 red connectors (C4)
  2 yellow connectors (C10)

6 white rods, (R2)
5 yellow rods (R4)
4 red rods (R6)
2 small tires (T1)
2 large tires (T2)
2 small wheels (W1)
2 large wheels (W2)
1 mousetrap
4 small washers
1 piece of string
1 piece of nylon line
1 piece of masking tape

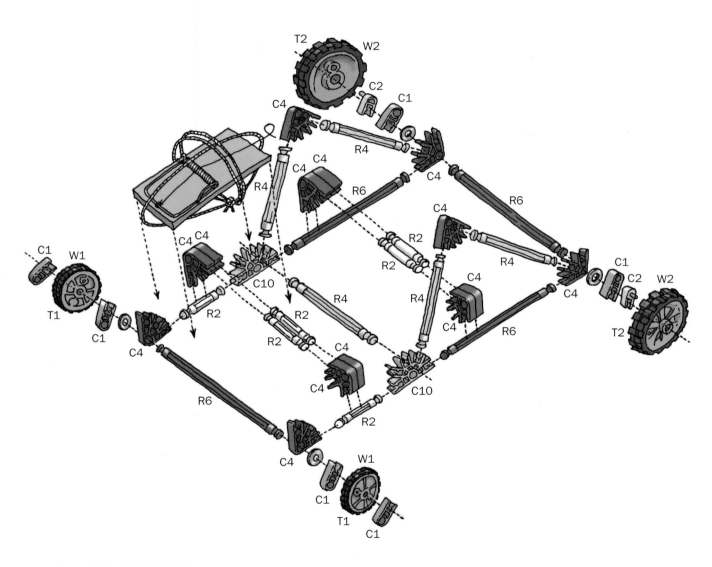

Figure 19.1 *Exploded view of the mousetrap car*

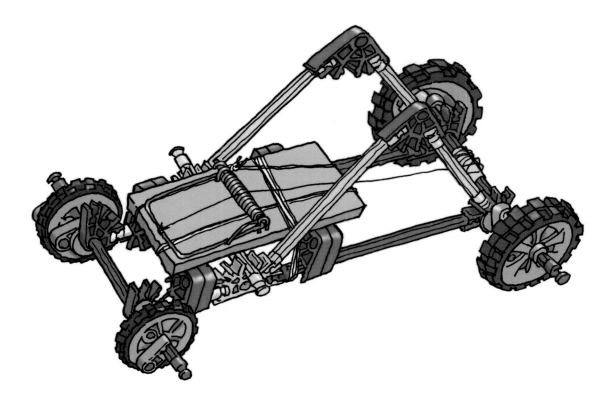

Figure 19.2 *Assembled mousetrap car. The mousetrap in this illustration has been sprung. The nylon line is attached to the jaws of the trap and to the rear axle. By turning the wheels, you can wind the nylon line around the axle and pull the jaws of the trap open.*

2. Double-check your vehicle to be sure that the trap is securely attached to the car and that the jaws of the mousetrap will open and close properly.

3. How can you put energy into the mousetrap car? Discuss this question with the class.

SAFETY TIP

Do not put your fingers in the clamping device of the mousetrap.

Inquiry 19.1
Observing the Motion of the Mousetrap Car

PROCEDURE

1. Complete the activities that follow. Record your observations and answers to the questions in your science notebook. Be prepared to share your observations with the class.

2. Set the car on the table or floor and attach a spring scale to the mousetrap bar. Holding the car firmly, slowly pull the bar back with the spring scale. Observe the force on the spring scale as you pull the bar. Record what happens to the force as you keep pulling the bar. Slowly release the bar so that it returns to its resting position; then remove the spring scale hook from the bar (see Figure 19.3).

3. Hold the car so that it does not touch the floor. Set the mousetrap spring by turning the wheels of the car so that the nylon line winds around the axle and pulls the mousetrap bar all the way back. Let go of the wheels while still holding the car off the floor. Do this several times. Describe what happens.

4. What do you think the motion of the car would be if you set the mousetrap and released it with the car on the floor? Write your prediction in your science notebook.

5. Reset the mousetrap. Place the car on the floor and release it. Describe what happens.

6. Write a paragraph describing the motions of the mousetrap car after the trap was set and the car was released. Discuss with your lab partner what forces you think are producing the motions.

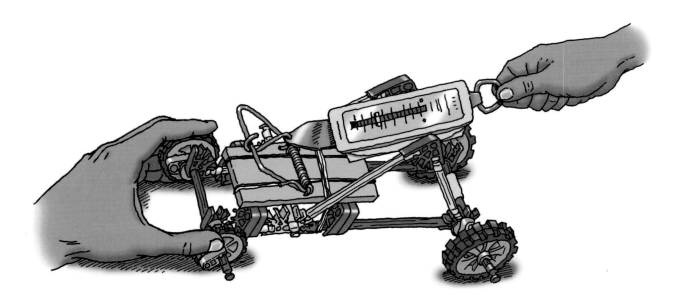

Figure 19.3 *Attach and pull the spring scale as shown here to measure the force of the mousetrap spring.*

Inquiry 19.2
Measuring the Speed of the Mousetrap Car

PROCEDURE

1. Share with the class what you wrote about the motion of your mousetrap car.

2. With the class, discuss the following questions:

  A. Is the speed of the car constant as it moves across the floor?

  B. How could you calculate the average speed of your car?

  C. How could you design an experiment to measure the speed of the mousetrap car as it travels along the floor?

3. With your group, develop a plan to measure the motion. Design an experiment to determine the mousetrap car's speed at different positions along its path. Write your plan in your science notebook. Design a data table on which to record your measurements and any calculations.

4. Carry out your plan.

5. When you are done, summarize the conclusions you can draw from your data.

6. Follow your teacher's instructions to disassemble your car and return the parts to storage.

REFLECTING ON WHAT YOU'VE DONE
Answer the following questions in your science notebook. Be prepared to share your answers with the class.

  A. Summarize what you found out about the motion of the car. Give evidence from your data for your conclusions.

  B. Explain the changes in the mousetrap car's speed in terms of the forces acting on the car.

  C. When you set the mousetrap, do you do work on it? If so, why?

  D. Write a paragraph describing the energy changes that took place when you set the trap and released the car.

  E. How does the motion of the mousetrap car compare with the motion of the fan car? Identify similarities and differences. What forces acted each time?

Rocket Science 101

Powerful rockets are needed to launch the Space Shuttle into orbit.

You don't need to be a rocket scientist to understand how a rocket works. All you need to know is Newton's Third Law of Motion, which states that for every action, there is an equal and opposite reaction.

Newton's Third Law of Motion works for all forces, including the ones you have been exploring in the lab. For example, when your fan car was running, the fan pushed on the air and the air pushed back on the fan. It was the air pushing on the fan that pushed the car. The air went one way and the car went the other.

Something similar happens with rockets. Rockets go forward by expelling hot gas backward. Rocket engines generate the force to push the gas out at very high speed by burning a lot of fuel quickly. Rapidly burning fuel creates the huge force that sends the hot gases out of the rocket. According to Newton's Third Law of Motion, as the rocket pushes the gas out the back, the gas pushes the rocket forward. Newton, in fact, knew that if something was launched with enough force, it could gain enough speed to orbit the earth or even to escape the earth, but he did not have rockets powerful enough to do it.

To launch a rocket, a rocket engine must expel its gases with enough force (thrust) to exceed the force of gravity. People had been using this principle for centuries. For example, the Chinese were using rockets for military purposes in the 13th century. The Chinese also invented fireworks, which are another example of rockets. These early rockets were powered by solid fuel, which was similar in composition to gunpowder.

In the early 1800s, a British officer, William Congreve,

improved existing rockets for military use. Their glow inspired the words "rockets' red glare" in "The Star-Spangled Banner," the national anthem of the United States. But none of these rockets was powerful enough to launch anything into space. Like the Chinese rockets, the rockets launched with this gunpowder-type fuel all fell back to the ground.

Launching satellites into orbit and sending them to other planets requires very powerful rockets. The force of the rockets must push on the satellites and give them enough speed so they will go around the earth continuously and not fall back to the ground. To send a spacecraft to the moon or to other planets in our solar system, the force of the rocket has to be strong enough, and last long enough, to give the spacecraft the speed to escape the earth and not be bound by its gravity. The speed needed to leave the earth and not be bound by its gravity is called escape velocity. Clearly, if space travel were to become a reality, scientists would need to find a way to make more powerful rockets.

It wasn't until 1926 that American physicist Robert Hutchings Goddard developed and launched the world's first liquid-fueled rocket. This breakthrough eventually led to

Fireworks are rockets, too.

the development of rockets powerful enough to launch satellites and other spacecraft into orbit around the earth. In 1957, Russia successfully launched Sputnik, the first artificial satellite. In 1958, the United States successfully launched a satellite into space. It was named *Explorer I*. These satellites orbited the earth and were a wonder of science and technology. They marked the beginning of the Space Age.

In the 1960s, scientists and

Left: *An early space rocket designed by Robert Goddard is prepared for launching.*

engineers in the United States developed and built Saturn V, the biggest and most powerful rocket ever built. It stood almost 20 meters higher than the Statue of Liberty; on the launch pad, it weighed 13 times more than the statue. The engines on the rocket had the horsepower of 4300 automobiles. Saturn V was used to send a three-man crew to the moon in 1969. It needed so much fuel that it was built in stages, or sections. Each stage was released when the fuel in it was used up. This process made the rocket lighter after each release so that it was easier to speed up the rocket and send its payload of astronauts on their way.

Rockets like the Saturn V are no longer being built. They are too expensive, and future manned missions would require rockets even more powerful than the Saturn V. But scientists and engineers continue to improve rocket technology. They are exploring new designs that will eventually enable humans to travel back to the moon and beyond. Someday, you will even be able to take a space vacation. (Book early. Reservations required.) ❑

QUESTIONS

1. What is the energy source for a rocket?
2. What energy changes take place in a rocket when it is launched?
3. How are the forces in a rocket similar to the forces in a mousetrap car? How are they different?

From 1968 to 1972, the Apollo mission sent
crews of astronauts to explore the moon.
Astronauts took this picture, which shows how
the earth looks as seen from the moon.

NASA

Medieval Warfare in Modern Times

A young man in leather armor and carrying a wooden shield runs from the fire of a catapult that is throwing missiles at him. Temporarily out of the catapult's range, he pauses to rest, checks his digital watch, and looks around at the Arizona landscape. Digital watch? Arizona? This man isn't a medieval warrior but a member of a war reenactment group in the 21st century. The catapult is built, as much as possible, like a medieval catapult. However, rather than throwing heavy stones, reenactment catapults throw groups of tennis balls that are taped together. (The word "catapult" comes from two Greek words: *kata* means "down" and *pallein* means "to hurl.")

Catapults were war machines during medieval times. They were used to attack castles and fortresses. The catapults hurled large stones and other things at the castle walls or even over the walls of fortresses. Persistent battering could eventually win the battle. Medieval warriors used at least three different kinds of catapults, and the people who participate in medieval battle reenactments today build and use all three of them.

One kind of catapult is the *mangonel*. The Romans designed it in the third century. It was the most popular kind of catapult of the medieval period. It is also the most popular catapult built for reenactments today. How does a mangonel work?

Setting a mangonel is very much like setting a giant mousetrap. A mangonel has a single arm with a cuplike extension at the end. Two ropes attached to this arm can be wound around a pole using a lever. As the ropes are wound

around the pole, the throwing arm is pulled down so that it can be loaded. The more tightly the rope is wound, the greater the force pulling on the throwing arm—the same as when you pull back the bar on a mousetrap. When the throwing arm is released, it snaps forward into a crossbar, which suddenly stops the throwing arm and sends a rock flying out of the cup and through the air. Unfortunately, this is an inefficient kind of catapult, since much of the available energy is lost into the framework of the catapult when the throwing arm hits the crossbar. Only a small portion of the energy put into the catapult when the ropes are stretched is converted to energy in moving the stone.

Medieval soldiers setting a mangonel for action

A second type of catapult from medieval times is called a *traction trebuchet*. With a long pole mounted on a tall frame, this catapult uses the principles of a lever. The pole is positioned so that the fulcrum is close to one end. A sling that holds a rock is attached to the end of the pole farthest from the fulcrum. Ropes are attached to the other end of the pole, which is at the end closest to the fulcrum. When a crew of warriors pulls down on these ropes at the end closest to the fulcrum, the long end of the pole rises quickly into the air and sends the rock hurtling toward the target.

In recent years, a crew of five people using a reconstructed traction trebuchet was able to throw a 900-gram lead ball 170 meters. Medieval traction trebuchets were known to have crews of 30 men or more.

A much more powerful catapult used in medieval times was the *counterweight trebuchet*. Like the traction trebuchet, the counterweight trebuchet uses the principles of a lever. However, gravity, rather than a crew of warriors, provides the downward force that sends the rock into the air. A heavy weight is attached to the short end of the pole. The longer end has to be pulled

The trebuchet was a kind of catapult. This one used counter-weights to fire its loads.

down by the crew and loaded before it can be used. When the long end of the pole is released, gravity pulls the heavy weight on the short end down. The long end is raised into the air, and the stone is sent flying. This design worked well; 44 such catapults spread havoc around Europe during medieval times. A modern counterweight trebuchet with a 5400-kilogram weight has been used to throw a 635-kilogram car 79 meters and 45 kilograms of iron 215 meters.

While catapults like these and others from medieval times are no longer used in war, they are still of great interest to a number of people. War-reenactment groups, historians, and others build them. Over the years, all sorts of items have been launched with catapults—from stones and spears to people, pianos, and pumpkins. ◻

Today people reenact medieval catapult launches in mock battles.

The Roller Coaster

The assembled roller coaster

© TERRY G. McCREA/SMITHSONIAN INSTITUTION

INTRODUCTION

In Lesson 2, you built a battery and saw evidence that it contained energy. You then observed how the energy it stored could be changed to other forms of energy. You found, for example, that it had the energy to light a bulb. In this lesson, you will build a roller coaster and a roller coaster car. You will test the roller coaster to make sure it works properly. In the next lesson, you will learn how to put energy into the roller coaster car. And you will investigate how the speed and energy of the car change as it moves on the track.

OBJECTIVE FOR THIS LESSON

Build a roller coaster.

Getting Started

1. Look at the photo on page 200, which shows an assembled roller coaster. You and your classmates will build a roller coaster just like this one. To do it, you need to divide the work among the members of your class and work cooperatively. Discuss a plan for developing student groups to work on different parts of the roller coaster. Each group should identify the part of the roller coaster it will assemble.

2. Check to see that your group has all the necessary K'NEX® pieces for its section of the roller coaster.

MATERIALS FOR LESSON 20

For the class

K'NEX® parts for the roller coaster and roller coaster car (see Appendix A: Directory of K'NEX® Parts):

  4 gray connectors (C1)

12 red connectors (C4)

12 green connectors (C5)

30 purple connectors (C6)

30 blue connectors (C7)

100 gold connectors (C8)

22 white connectors (C9)

  8 yellow connectors (C10)

50 green rods (R1)

22 white rods (R2)

46 blue rods (R3)

20 yellow rods (R4)

70 gold rods (R5)

42 red rods (R6)

40 gray rods (R7)

  4 large wheels (W2)

  2 4.25-m strips of K'NEX® track

Inquiry 20.1
Building a Roller Coaster

PROCEDURE

1. Figures 20.1 through 20.6 show how to assemble and connect the sides of the roller coaster. Each student group will assemble and connect the two sides needed for each section. Figure 20.7 shows how to connect the two sides of the roller coaster using the gold rods (R5). Figures 20.8 through 20.10 show how to assemble and connect the completed sections. Use the illustrations that match the sections your group is assembling. The orange track shown in the illustrations is attached after all sections have been connected. Figures 20.11 and 20.12 show what the finished roller coaster looks like. Figure 20.13 shows how to assemble the roller coaster car and what the completed car will look like.

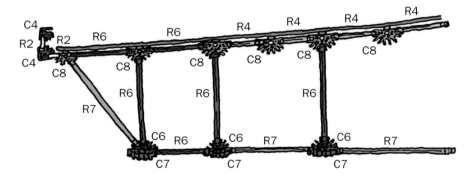

Figure 20.1 *Roller coaster, Section 1*

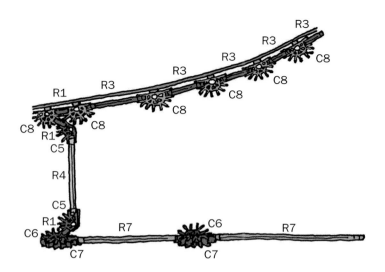

Figure 20.2 *Roller coaster, Section 2*

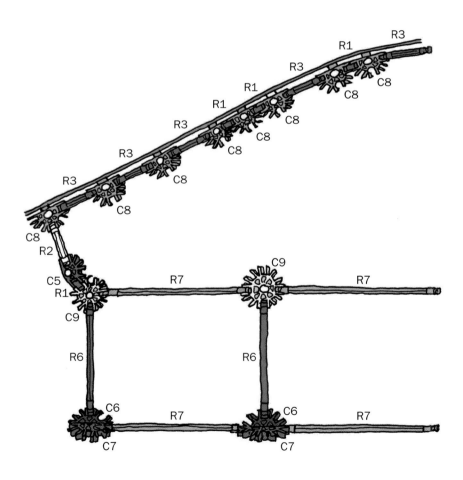

Figure 20.3 *Roller coaster, Section 3*

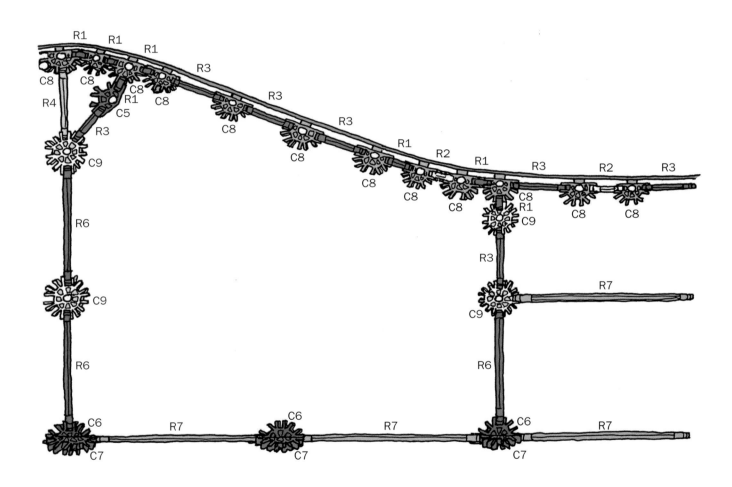

Figure 20.4 *Roller coaster, Section 4*

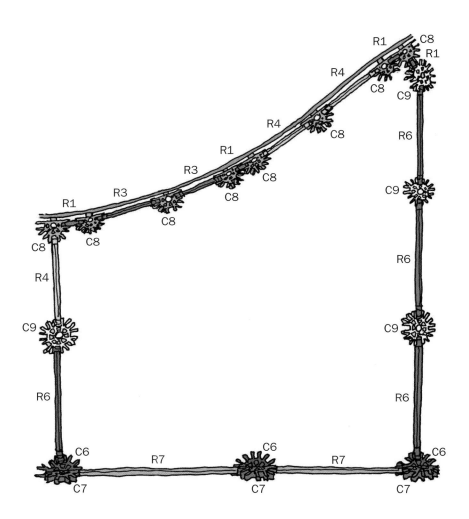

Figure 20.5 *Roller coaster, Section 5*

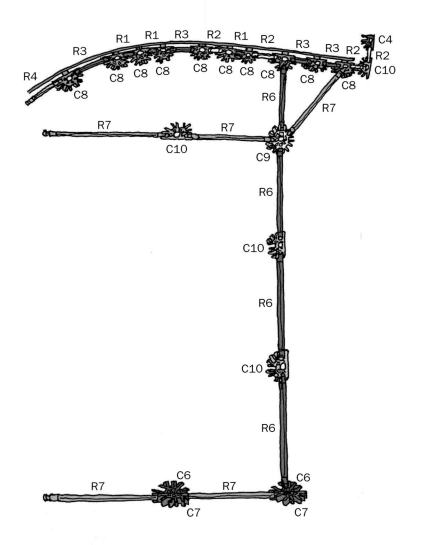

Figure 20.6 *Roller coaster, Section 6*

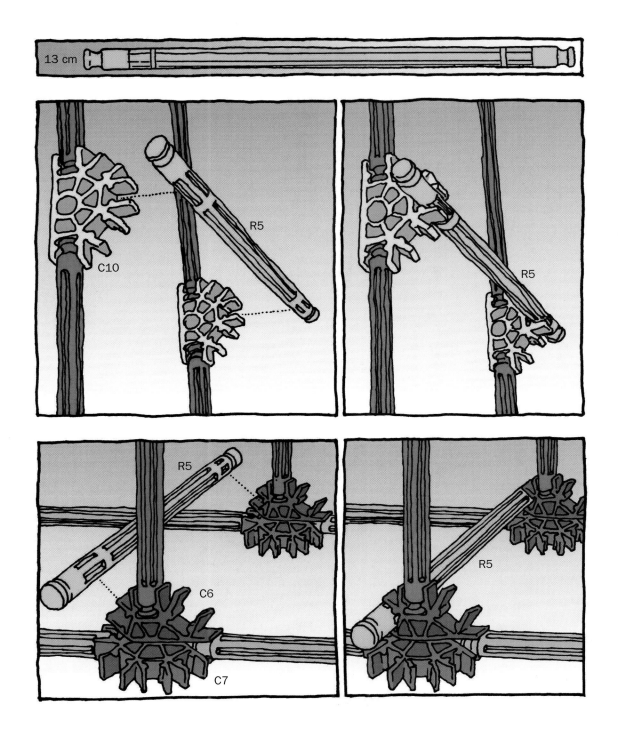

Figure 20.7 *How to connect gold rods to the roller coaster*

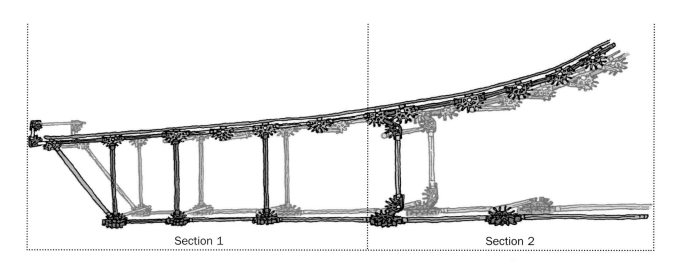

Figure 20.8 *Roller coaster A (Sections 1 and 2 connected)*

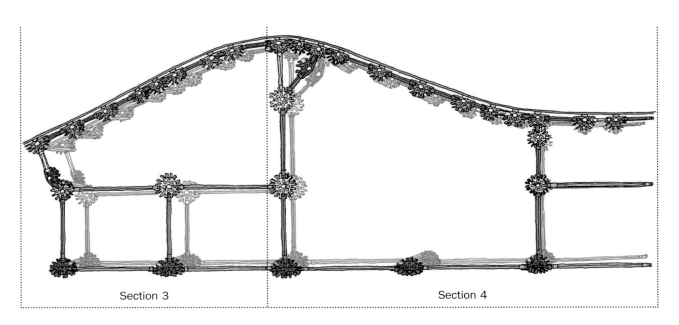

Section 3   Section 4

Figure 20.9 *Roller coaster B (Sections 3 and 4 connected)*

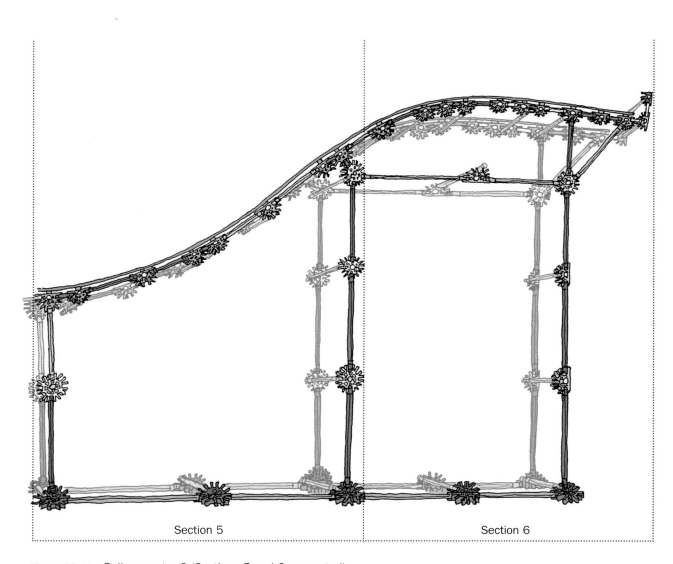

Figure 20.10 *Roller coaster C (Sections 5 and 6 connected)*

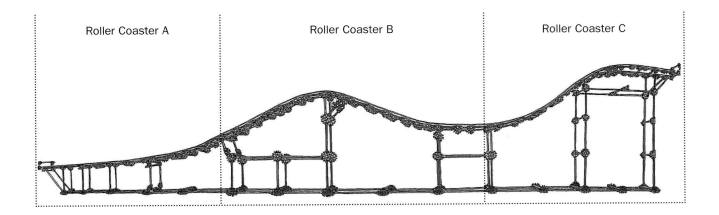

Figure 20.11   *Finished roller coaster, showing A, B, and C connected*

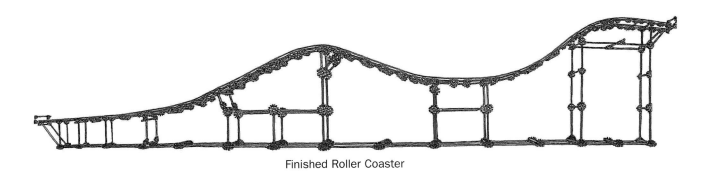

Finished Roller Coaster

Figure 20.12   *Finished roller coaster*

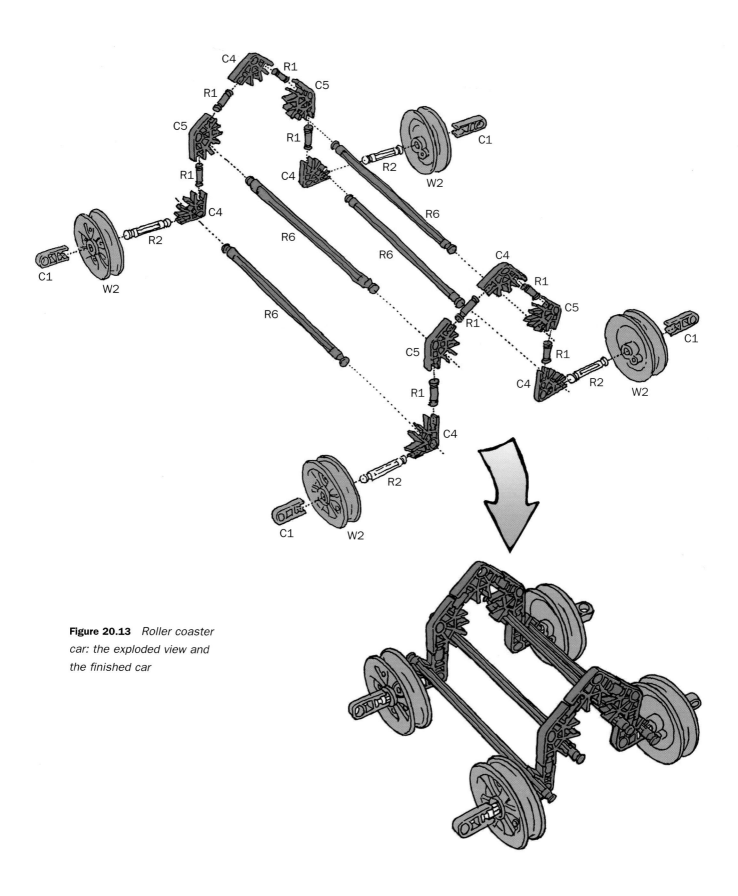

Figure 20.13 *Roller coaster car: the exploded view and the finished car*

2. After each group has connected its section of roller coaster, the group responsible for the track should attach the track to each side of the roller coaster. The track must be stretched smoothly and tightly along the coaster frame. Appendix A has tips for putting the track on the roller coaster.

3. The group that built the roller coaster car should then place the car on the roller coaster at the high end of the track and test the car to make sure that it coasts smoothly and remains on the track for the entire length of the roller coaster. If the car does not move smoothly, check to see that all the parts are connected correctly and that the track is attached smoothly.

REFLECTING ON WHAT YOU'VE DONE

1. In your science notebook, describe your contribution to the class's task of building the roller coaster.

2. Now place the roller coaster car at the low end of the roller coaster track. Describe the motion of the car.

3. Discuss with the class ways to put energy in the car so that it will move along the track.

4. Discuss with the class how roller coasters in amusement parks get the energy they need to move along the track.

Motion on a Roller Coaster

The laws of physics in action!

PHOTO BY DAN FEICHT, CEDAR POINT AMUSEMENT PARK/RESORT

INTRODUCTION

When you enjoy the thrill of a ride on a roller coaster, you are experiencing the laws of physics and energy and motion in action. In this lesson, you will use the roller coaster and roller coaster car your class built in Lesson 20. You will investigate energy transformations as the roller coaster car moves along the roller coaster track. You will also compare the motion of the roller coaster car with the motions of the fan car and the mousetrap car that you built in previous lessons.

OBJECTIVES FOR THIS LESSON

Observe and describe the motion of the roller coaster car as it moves along the roller coaster track.

Predict the motion of the roller coaster car when it is released at different points along the track.

Measure the speed of the roller coaster car at several points on the track.

Describe the energy changes in the roller coaster car as it moves along the track.

Getting Started

1. If you have not read "Potential and Kinetic Energy" on pages 216–217, read it at this time.

2. On the basis of what you read in "Potential and Kinetic Energy," answer the following questions in your science notebook:

   A. *What does it mean for something to have potential energy?*

   B. *If a book weighs 15.0 N, what is its gain in gravitational potential energy when it is lifted onto a shelf 2.0 m above the floor?*

   C. *How can you tell whether something has kinetic energy?*

   D. *Do you ever have kinetic energy? How do you get it? How do you lose it?*

3. Have your science notebook ready so you can write your predictions, observations, and answers in it as you perform the inquiry.

MATERIALS FOR LESSON 21

For the class
1 roller coaster
1 roller coaster car
1 0- to 10-N spring scale
1 meterstick
1 student timer
1 piece of masking tape

POTENTIAL AND KINETIC ENERGY

You have investigated energy and changes in energy throughout this module. You have seen how energy can be stored in batteries and springs. You have also seen how energy can be transformed into different forms, such as light, heat, motion, and electrical energy.

Storing Energy

When work is done on something, its energy changes. For instance, when you set the spring in the mousetrap car, you did work on the spring because you exerted a force on the spring when you wound it around the axle of the car. The spring gained energy and stored it for later use. Scientists call this stored energy *potential energy.*

When you let go of the car, the spring released the potential energy. The force of the spring did work on the mousetrap car and increased its speed. The stored energy in the spring became *kinetic energy,* or energy of motion. Some of the energy in the spring also became heat energy because of friction. Eventually, friction stopped the car, and the kinetic energy of the car was transformed into *heat energy.*

The batteries you used earlier in this module also stored energy. The batteries stored the energy as *chemical potential energy* that became *electric potential energy.* When the batteries were connected in a circuit, the electric potential energy was transformed to other forms of energy in lightbulbs and motors.

Energy can be stored in other ways, too. You can store energy in an object by lifting it. Whenever you pick up an object, you do work on it, because your muscles exert a force on an object through a distance. Your muscles changed the chemical energy in your body into energy in the lifted object. But what kind of energy is associated with the lifted object?

Gravitational Potential Energy

The energy an object gains when it is lifted is called *gravitational potential energy.* It is called *gravitational* potential energy because you must work against gravity to lift an object to a higher position above the ground (earth). Any object above the ground has gravitational potential energy that can be released.

The amount of gravitational potential energy an object has depends on how much it weighs and how high above the ground it is. For example, it hurts more if a heavy book falls from your desk and hits your foot than if a light book falls and hits you from that same height. If you drop the same book from different heights, however, you will find that the higher the book's starting position, the more your foot hurts when the book hits it.

To calculate the gravitational potential energy of an object, you multiply its weight by its height above the ground, as shown in the following equation:

$$\text{Gravitational potential energy} = \text{Weight} \times \text{Height}$$

Weight is measured in newtons, and height is measured in meters; therefore, the unit of measure for potential energy is newton-meters. Newton-meters are also called joules. Thus, the units for energy are the same as the units for work. Remember: *Energy is the ability to do work.*

Kinetic Energy

Moving objects have another kind of energy. It is called *energy of motion,* or *kinetic energy.* Any time an object moves, it has kinetic energy. The kinetic energy of an object depends on how fast it is moving and how much mass it has. The greater the speed of an object, the greater its kinetic energy. The greater the mass of an object, the greater its kinetic energy.

Kinetic energy is also measured in newton-meters, or joules. In fact, all forms of energy can be measured using these units.

In this lesson, you will study how gravitational potential energy and kinetic energy change as a car travels along a roller coaster. You will learn how to put gravitational potential energy in the car, and you will observe how energy converts from one form to another as the car moves along the track.

Inquiry 21.1
Observing the Motion of a Roller Coaster Car

PROCEDURE

1. Discuss the following questions with your group. Then share your answers with the class.

  A. *What kind of energy would the roller coaster car gain if you lifted it to the top of the roller coaster?*

  B. *How does it get this energy?*

2. Before you place the roller coaster car on the track, make the following predictions about what the speed of the car would be if it were released from the top of the track:

  A. *At what point along the track will the car have the fastest speed? The slowest speed? Why do you think so?*

  B. *Where will the car have its greatest kinetic energy?*

  C. *How do you think the car gained its kinetic energy?*

  D. *Is it possible for the car to have both kinds of energy anywhere on the track?*

3. Place the car at the highest point on the roller coaster track. Let it roll down. Compare your observations of its motion with your predictions. Discuss this with your group.

4. On the basis of your observations and what you have learned about energy, discuss with the class why the car moves the way it does along the track.

5. Predict what the motion would be if you were to place the car at the top of the lower hill and allow it to move back toward the higher hill.

6. Test your prediction by observing the car's motion. Answer this question in your science notebook: On the basis of what you have learned about energy, how do you account for the car's motion when the car is released from the lower hill? Then discuss your ideas with the class.

Inquiry 21.2
Measuring the Speed of the Roller Coaster Car

PROCEDURE

1. You will measure the roller coaster car's speed at different points along the track. Before you make speed measurements, consider these questions:

  A. *What force "pulls" on the car as it moves along the track?*

  B. *Do any other forces act on the car as it moves along the track? If so, what are they? How do they affect the motion?*

2. Use a spring scale to measure the weight of the roller coaster car.

3. How much work must you do to lift the car from the tabletop to the top of the highest hill on the roller coaster? Write out your calculation.

4. Working with your group, develop a plan to measure the speed of the car from at least three different points along the roller coaster track. Determine how the speed of the car changes as it moves along the track.

5. Carry out your plan. Be sure to discuss the following questions:

   A. How did your group select points along the track? What methods did your classmates use?

   B. How did your speed values compare with those of the other groups?

REFLECTING ON WHAT YOU'VE DONE

1. Write responses to the following questions in your science notebook:

   A. What have you learned about the motion of the roller coaster car as it moves along the track?

   B. What energy changes took place as the car moved along the track?

   C. What changes could you make in the roller coaster to make the roller coaster car go faster?

   D. How does the motion of the roller coaster car compare with the motion of the fan car and the mousetrap car? How are these motions alike? How are they different?

2. Discuss your answers with the class.

Twists, Turns, and Loops

Kuh-chink, kuh-chink, kuh-chink. The train lurches slowly up the first hill of the roller coaster. You give the lap bar one last tug. Then you round the first corner, pick up speed, and … Aaaaaaggghh!

You may not be thinking about the fundamentals of physics while you're riding a roller coaster. But those fundamentals, especially the laws dealing with energy and motion, are what keep you in your seat. They ensure that your ride is safe—as well as fun.

A roller coaster is a fairly simple machine. A chain that is attached to a motor pulls a train of cars filled with people to the top of a steep hill. When the cars are released, the thrills begin!

At the top of the hill, a roller coaster train and its riders have a large amount of stored, or potential, energy. The work the motor did to drag its load against the force of gravity to the top of the hill stored energy in the train and riders as it pulled them to the top. The higher the hill and the more work the motor did, the more gravitational potential energy it stored in the train and riders.

When the train and riders crest the hill and begin to rush downward, their gravitational potential energy begins turning into kinetic energy. The shape of the track and the height of the hills control the train's changes in speed and direction.

PHOTO BY DAN FEICHT, CEDAR POINT AMUSEMENT PARK/RESORT

Each roller coaster uses different combinations of twists, turns, dips, and dives to convert gravitational potential energy into kinetic energy.

Going around a loop on a roller coaster. The tighter the loop, the harder your seat pushes against you. Why?

As the train and riders descend farther and farther, more and more gravitational potential energy turns to kinetic energy. That means the train and riders go faster and faster. As they rise, the train and riders gain back some of their gravitational potential energy and lose kinetic energy and slow down. Tight curves, which provide sudden direction changes, add to the thrills.

The first roller coasters were made from wood. They were not as efficient in converting potential energy into kinetic energy as today's coasters are. Roller coasters made of steel do a better job because there is less energy lost to heat and more energy to be spent on thrills.

Other improvements have been made in roller coaster design. Most of today's steel coasters include at least one bit of looped track that momentarily turns your world upside down. The looped track exerts a force on the train cars and on you and the other riders that sends you around the loop. Many coasters have multiple loops and corkscrews to maximize the fun.

Finally, your ride is over. You've been up and down and all around—a very energetic experience indeed! ☐

Energy and sudden turns provide plenty of thrills as you ride the coaster.

ISAAC NEWTON GOES SKIING

This cross-country skier may not know it, but Newton's laws of motion are at work.

We don't know whether Sir Isaac Newton ever tried skiing. It's entirely possible, because skis were invented before his birth in 1642. Skis have been in use for more than 2000 years—long before Newton ever thought about gravity or came up with his laws of motion.

Even though Newton may never have made the connection between skiing and his three laws of motion, you can. In fact, knowing Newton's laws of motion is useful if you go skiing. Knowing about gravity helps too.

The First Law

Take Newton's First Law of Motion: An object at rest will remain at rest, and an object in motion will remain in motion with the same speed and direction, unless acted upon by an outside force. That means it takes a force to start you moving and another force to make you stop. You also need to apply a force if you want to change the direction in which you're moving. If no forces act on you, you just keep moving along at the same speed and in the same direction.

How does this apply to skiing? If you're skiing across flat terrain (cross-country skiing), you have to exert a force to get yourself moving. You do that by pushing with your poles. You keep moving because there is not much friction (an outside force) to work against you and bring you to a stop. (To make the friction even less, you can wax your skis.) To change direction, you have to push with both your poles and legs to turn your skis.

The Second Law

How hard do you have to push to get going? It depends on your mass— that is, the amount of matter in your body. The more you ate for lunch, the harder you'll have to push to get going quickly. This is a skier's way of using Newton's Second Law of Motion: The acceleration (rate of speeding up or slowing down) of an object depends upon the mass of the object and the force acting upon it.

You can start moving by pushing with a small force, but it will take you longer to reach the same speed than if you'd pushed harder. Regardless of how you choose to get going, what you're doing is putting to work some of that chemical potential energy from the food you ate at lunch and changing it into kinetic energy.

The Third Law

After you are in motion, you can coast for quite a long time, unless you hit another skier… or a tree! If you collide with another skier on the slopes, you may bounce off each other before coming to a stop. Newton had a law for that, too. It's his Third Law of Motion: For every action, there is an equal and opposite reaction.

What Else Is Happening?

As you glide down those slopes, forces other than the ones you exert are helping you. One of them—you guessed it—is gravity. Gravity works in your favor when it comes to down-hill skiing. In downhill skiing, you've got the whole mass of the earth helping you along.

The rate at which you speed up depends on a number of things, including the angle of the slope, how slippery your skis are, and another force—the friction created between your body and the air as you race along.

The smaller the amount of friction, the faster you'll accelerate. If you're wearing tight ski gear, you'll go even faster.

The whole time you're going downhill, gravity is working to change your gravitational potential energy into kinetic energy.

What happens when you ski uphill? Gravity works against your upward motion, and you slow down. If the hill is higher than the one you start-ed on, you won't make it to the top. If the second hill is lower than the one you started on, however, you have enough energy to go up and over the top and start down again.

Skillful use of opposing forces lets you come to a safe stop.

Downhill skiers enjoy the ride as gravity transforms potential energy into kinetic energy.

reducing your speed is to turn your skis so that they dig into the snow.

Would an understanding of the laws of motion, of gravity, and of friction have helped Sir Isaac be a better skier? It's hard to say. Skiing is one sport that requires a good deal of skill and athletic ability. But knowing what's happening as you glide along is a definite advantage. Sir Isaac might not have had skills equal to those of an Olympic contender, but he probably would have managed to keep his balance, even when his wig was blowing in the wind. ☐

QUESTION

In what ways is skiing like riding a roller coaster?

When you're skiing, why can it be so hard to stop? One reason is that there's not much friction between the icy slopes and your well-waxed skis. Since there is not much friction, you just keep on going. If you want to stop, you have to apply a force against your motion. That means that, at least if you're like most first-time skiers, you fall when you're trying to come to a graceful stop.

At that moment, friction kicks in. The friction between your body and the snow slows you down. Your kinetic energy is converted to heat—so much heat, in fact, that as you slide, your body melts some of the snow! A more expert method of

22
The Anchor Activity

An oral presentation is an important part of your Anchor Activity.

INTRODUCTION

Over the past several weeks, you have been either investigating how a device works or building a device of your own. Now you will share what you learned with your classmates and find out what they learned as well. In this lesson, you will display your poster or computer-generated program. You will also give an oral presentation to the class. Sharing knowledge is a key element of the scientific process.

OBJECTIVES FOR THIS LESSON

Display your poster or computer program showing what you learned about the device you selected to explore for the Anchor Activity.

Demonstrate how your device works.

Give an oral presentation about your device.

Inquiry 22.1
Presentations for the Class

PROCEDURE

1. Your teacher will give you guidelines for displaying your poster or computer-generated presentation. Keep in mind that you may want to use this display as part of your oral presentation.

2. Your teacher will organize the order of the presentations for your class. Make sure you have everything you need for your presentation. Review Inquiry Master 17.1b, which describes the guidelines for the oral presentation, so you will know how your teacher will be assessing your presentation.

3. Listen to your classmates' presentations. As you listen, think about how what they did was like what you did. Also think about how what they did was different from what you did.

4. Complete Student Sheet 22.1: Self-Assessment.

MATERIALS FOR LESSON 22

For you
1 copy of Student Sheet 22.1: Self-Assessment

UNUSUAL INVENTIONS

Alexander Graham Bell patented his design for the first telephone in 1876. The new device caught on quickly. By the turn of the 20th century, the U.S. Patent and Trademark Office had granted more than 100 patents for telephones. By 1946, the first mobile telephone service was started.

While some patented inventions, such as the telephone, quickly earn a place in homes and offices around the world, others never achieve that popularity. Here are drawings of two patented inventions. Look at each of them. What do you think the invention was designed to do? When you've made up your mind, turn the page and read the descriptions to see whether you were correct.

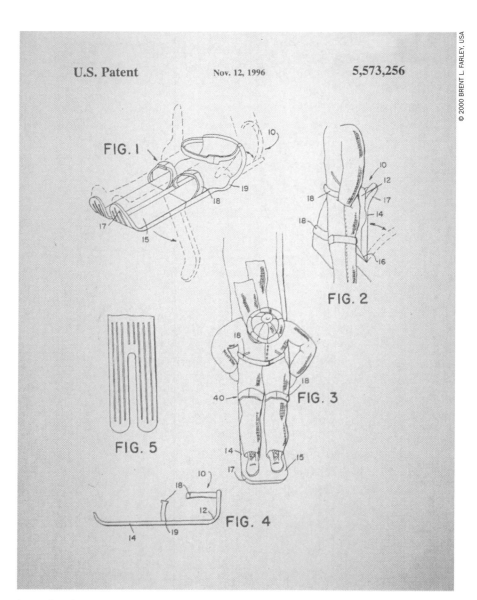

Invention A

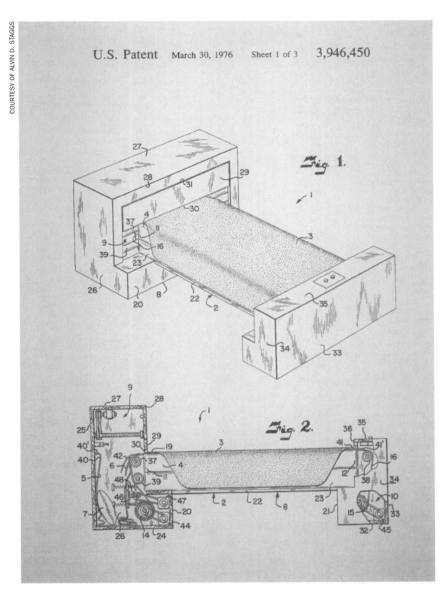

Invention B

Invention A, shown in the photo on page 228, is a pair of sled pants. They are designed to spare people the job of carrying their sleds back up a hill. The pants are attached by a series of bands. The flap shown at the bottom of the drawing can be folded up for walking. When the flap is unfolded, it forms part of the sled.

Invention B is a bed-making device. It automatically removes a bedspread and replaces it with sheets and a pillow when the bed is about to be used. In the morning, the device pulls off the sheets and pillow and puts the bedspread back on the bed. Wouldn't you like to have one of these the next time your parents ask you to clean your room? □

QUESTIONS

1. Sometimes a good name can be the secret to a successful invention. What would you name the inventions described?
2. Are you surprised that neither of the inventions described in this reader caught on? Why or why not?
3. What factors contribute to a successful invention?

BUILDING A BETTER BICYCLE RACK

The Man Behind Patent Number 3,847,317

Scientist Bob Burruss already has three patents, and he has two additional patent applications on file. When you talk to Bob about his inventions, you get insight into how scientists think and work, as well as a better understanding of the patent application process in the United States.

Bob holds a degree in mechanical engineering, and he's worked in that field since graduating from college. Experimenting with ideas, however, is not something that requires a college degree, in Bob's opinion. "A lot of science is just 'messing around,'" he says. In his case, the desire to "tinker" began by the age of four.

When Bob was still in grade school, a middle school teacher encouraged his interest in science. "I'd drop by her class every afternoon after school," he says. The teacher was a "generalist," and Bob bombarded her with questions about weather, space, and geology.

By the time Bob turned 16, school science fairs were among his favorite activities. He built an award-winning jet engine from scratch. He even had to teach himself to weld in the process.

The approach he took to that high school project has been helpful throughout his life. If you're interested in science, Bob says, you have to learn by doing. "The only thing that comes from books is information. Actual knowledge comes only from doing," he says.

Tinkering is one thing. But where new designs and inventions are concerned, how does an idea become reality? Bob's experience with one of his patents helps answer this question.

Inventor Bob Burruss

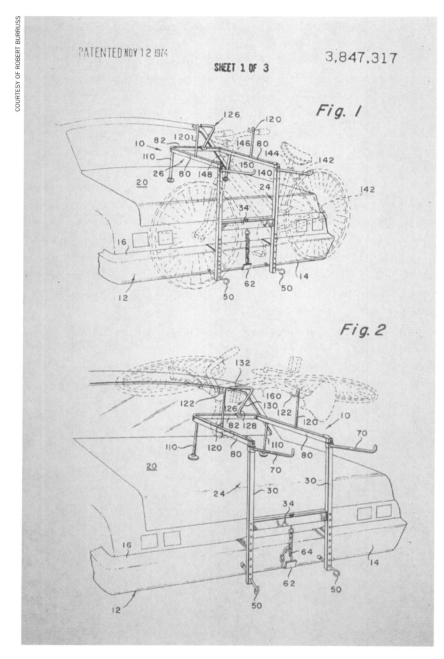

To obtain a patent, a drawing or diagram of the invention must be submitted. This is the diagram for the bike rack Bob Burruss invented.

In the 1970s, Bob worked for an engineering consulting firm. One day, his boss came by with a challenge. He asked Bob to design a car rack that could carry four bicycles. "No problem,"

said Bob. "I'll have a design ready for you tomorrow."

He made a design. His boss liked it. Bob's next assignment was to spend a month developing a prototype of the rack. The cost of the prototype could be no more than $200.

When the prototype model was completed, the next step was to design a production model. This time around, Bob's goal was to make sure his design had as few parts as possible and could be assembled easily.

Bob continued to work on his production model. He knew the price was right. It could be easily assembled. But he was concerned about one important thing: How many people would buy a four-bicycle rack? Would the rack have a market? Only time would tell.

In the meantime, Bob and his boss, Samuel Raff, applied for the patent. It was granted on November 12, 1974. The patent number was 3,847,317.

One thousand bicycle racks were produced. Unfortunately, Bob's prediction about the marketability of his new product was true. Only 200 of them were sold. Nevertheless, it was a success story for Bob. "It was exciting to see those racks being used," he says. "It was great to see my idea actually being used by people."

Getting a Patent: What's Involved?

What is involved in getting a patent? It's not too expensive, but it does take some work.

Today, inventors often begin by applying for a provisional patent. It is good for one year and gives the patent holder coverage in most countries of the world. For an individual, it costs $75 (companies pay more). The provisional patent, issued by the U.S. Patent and Trademark Office of the United States Government, protects the applicant's idea from being used by someone else. The inventor must submit notes and a sketch of the design. Inventors cannot talk about a new product or write anything about it until they hold a provisional patent. When the provisional patent has been granted, they can use the words "Patent Pending" if they are trying to sell their idea.

Applying for a final patent is more complicated. The inventor must follow a specific written format and provide a drawing that meets detailed specifications. A key part of the application is the "claims" section, in which the inventor defines the invention. The cost of filing a final patent application is $475 for private inventors.

A patent gives the inventor the right to prevent anyone else from making or selling the device in the United States for up to 20 years.

By the way, if you've got a bright idea and want to get a patent, there's no need to wait. You don't need to be an adult to file a patent application. The youngest patent holder is a four-year-old girl from Texas. Her patent is for a device that makes it easier to grab round knobs! ☐

QUESTIONS

1. What human need did Bob Burruss's invention meet?
2. What were the design constraints for his invention?
3. Can you think of something that would be a good invention? What would you have to do to get a patent for it?

The completed bike rack. You can carry up to four bikes with this rack—very handy for families who bike together.

COURTESY OF ROBERT BURRUSS

Appendix A
Directory of K'NEX® Parts

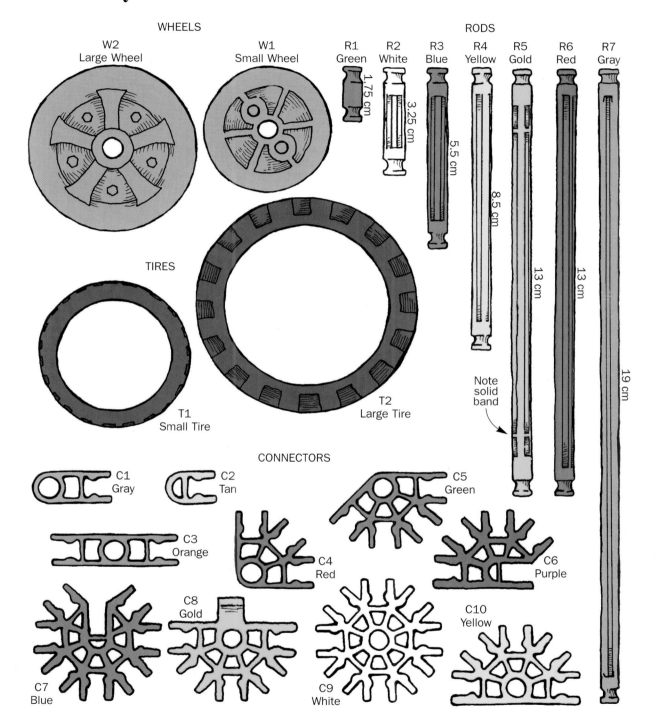

WHEELS

W2
Large Wheel

W1
Small Wheel

RODS

R1 Green
R2 White
R3 Blue
R4 Yellow
R5 Gold
R6 Red
R7 Gray

1.75 cm

3.25 cm

5.5 cm

8.5 cm

13 cm

13 cm

19 cm

Note solid band

TIRES

T1
Small Tire

T2
Large Tire

CONNECTORS

C1 Gray

C2 Tan

C3 Orange

C4 Red

C5 Green

C6 Purple

C7 Blue

C8 Gold

C9 White

C10 Yellow

Tips for Assembly of K'NEX® Parts

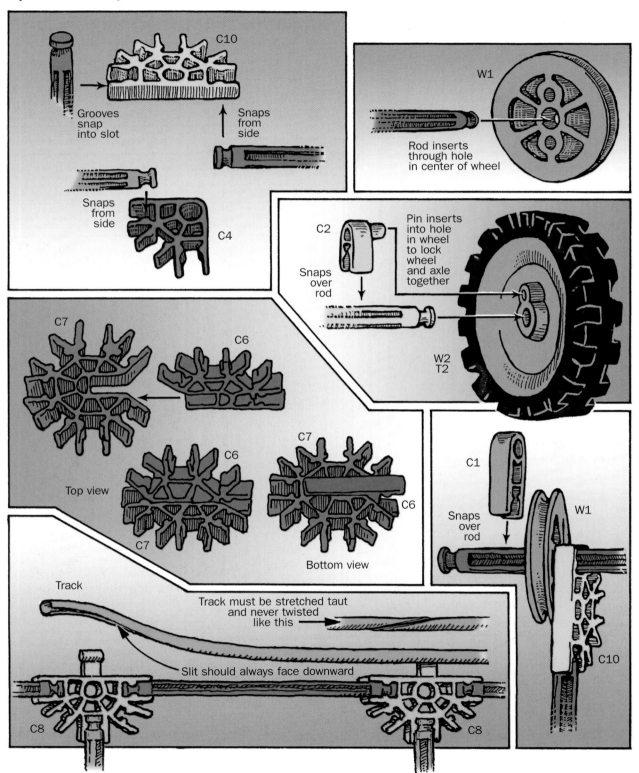

Glossary

actual mechanical advantage: The ratio of load force to effort force for a simple machine; indicates how much a machine multiples the effort force.

battery: A device, usually made of a container that holds two metal electrodes set in an electrolyte, that transforms chemical energy into electrical energy. *See* **dry cell; wet cell; rechargeable battery.**

dependent variable: The variable in an experiment whose value is determined by the experiment. *See also* **independent variable.**

dry cell: A battery cell made of two electrodes placed in an electrolyte that is a paste. *See also* **wet cell.**

efficiency: The ratio of output work to input work for a machine. The ratio value tells how well a machine does its work.

effort arm: The distance from the pivot point (fulcrum) to the point at which the effort force is applied on the arm of a lever.

effort distance: The distance over which the effort force acts in a simple machine.

effort force: The force exerted by a person (or motor) when using a machine to lift a load.

elastic force: The force exerted by elastic materials such as rubber bands and springs.

electric motor: A device that transforms electrical energy into mechanical energy.

electrode: A strip or rod (usually metal) set in the electrolyte in a battery. An electrode makes up one terminal of a battery.

electrolyte: A liquid or paste, often an acid, in which the electrodes of a battery are set.

energy: The ability to do work. Energy exists in many forms, such as chemical, mechanical, electrical, thermal, nuclear, kinetic, and light.

experimental control: A variable or quantity that is not changed during an experimental procedure, while other quantities are changed.

experimental design: The process of planning an experiment or procedure to investigate a scientific question.

force: A push or pull.

friction: A force that opposes the motion of an object. Examples include sliding friction and air friction. Sliding friction opposes the motion of objects across a surface. Air friction opposes the motion of objects moving through the air.

fulcrum: The pivot or fixed point around which a lever rotates.

gravity: The force of attraction between all matter. Because of gravity, the earth attracts other objects and pulls them toward its center.

heat energy: The energy that determines an object's temperature. Changes in an object's temperature or phase indicate a gain or loss of heat energy.

horsepower: Unit of power in the English system that is equal to approximately 750 watts.

ideal mechanical advantage: The ratio of effort distance to load distance for a simple machine. It is calculated by dividing the effort distance by the load distance.

inclined plane: A ramp or board positioned with one end higher than the other end. It is used to raise or lower objects by moving a load along the surface.

independent variable: The variable in an experiment that the experimenter changes.

input work: The work done by the effort force in a simple machine or motor. Input work is calculated by multiplying effort force by effort distance. *See also* **output work.**

joule (J): Unit of work and energy in the metric system.

kilogram (kg): Unit of mass in the metric system.

kinetic energy: Energy associated with moving bodies. Kinetic energy is calculated by multiplying one-half by the mass of an object and by the square of its speed.

lever: A rod or similar object that rotates around a pivot point and that can be used to do work.

load arm: The distance from the pivot point (fulcrum) to the point where the load is attached to the arm of a lever.

load distance: The distance a load moves when acted on by a load force.

load force: The force a machine exerts to lift a load. When lifting an object straight up, the load force is equal to the weight of the object.

machine: A device that can do work and, because of its mechanical advantage, can reduce the size of the effort force needed to do the work. *See* **actual mechanical advantage; ideal mechanical advantage.**

mass: The measure of the amount of matter in a body. The mass of a body determines how much it will accelerate when unbalanced forces act on it and how much it weighs at the earth's surface. In the metric system, mass is measured in kilograms or grams.

newton (N): Unit of force in the metric system.

output work: The work done on a load by a machine or motor. Output work is the product of load force and load distance. *See also* **input work.**

potential energy: Stored energy that can be released, includes chemical, electrical, gravitational, and nuclear energy.

power: The rate of doing work or the rate of changing energy. Power is calculated by dividing work done by the time required to do the work.

pulley: A wheel or cylinder with a rope around its outer rim. Used to do work to lift loads.

rechargeable battery: A battery that can be placed in a battery charger so that energy can be stored in it for later use. Rechargeable batteries can transform electrical energy into chemical energy. *See also* **battery.**

spring scale: A calibrated spring used to measure forces.

speed: A measure of how fast something is moving. The average speed of an object over a distance is the distance it moves divided by the time it takes to move that distance.

technological design: The process of designing solutions and building devices to meet human needs.

watt (W): The unit of power in the metric system. One watt is equal to 1 joule per second.

weight: The measure of the force of gravity on an object. Weight can be measured in newtons or pounds.

wet cell: A battery cell made of two electrodes placed in a liquid electrolyte. *See also* **dry cell.**

work: The product of a force and the distance through which it acts. *See also* **input work; output work.**

Index

Photo Credits

156 (top) © Jim Byrne/QA Photos **(bottom)** CORBIS/ Dave Bartruff **161 (top)** CORBIS/Roger Ressmeyer **(bottom)** CORBIS/Kevin R. Morris

Part 3 Motion **162–163** © Terry G. McCrea/Smithsonian Institution **164** CORBIS/Bettmann **168–170** Photo by Marvin D. Blimline/Maryland State Highway Administration **171 (top and bottom)** Rube Goldberg is the Registered Trademark and Copyright of Rube Goldberg, Inc. **172** Hagley Museum and Library **173** AP/WIDE WORLD PHOTOS **174** © Terry G. McCrea/Smithsonian Institution **181 (top and bottom)** NASA **182 (top)** CORBIS/Dan Guravich **(bottom)** CORBIS/Raymond Gebman **183 (top)** CORBIS **(bottom)** CORBIS/Hulton-Deutsch Collection **184** © Sovfoto/Eastfoto/PNI **185** CORBIS/Kelly-Mooney Photography **186** NASA **188** © Terry G. McCrea/Smithsonian Institution **194** NASA **195** AP/WIDE WORLD PHOTOS **196 (left)** CORBIS/Bettmann **(right)** NASA **198** CORBIS/Bettmann **199 (top)** CORBIS/Archivo Iconografico, S.A. **(bottom)** CORBIS/Charles & Josette Lenars **200** © Terry G. McCrea/Smithsonian Institution **214, 220, 221 (top and bottom)** Photo by Dan Feicht, Cedar Point Amusement Park/Resort **222** CORBIS/Galen Rowell **224** AP/WIDE WORLD PHOTOS **225** CORBIS/Karl Weatherly **226** © Terry G. McCrea/ Smithsonian Institution **228** © 2000 Brent L. Farley, USA **229** Courtesy of Alvin D. Staggs **231–233** Courtesy of Robert Burruss